CAREERS

in Focus

Arts
and
Entertainment

Ferguson Publishing Company
Chicago, Illinois

Copyright © 1998 Ferguson Publishing Company
ISBN 0-89434-245-2

Library of Congress Cataloging-in-Publication Data

Careers in Focus.   Arts and entertainment
    p.   cm.
  Includes index.
  Summary: Defines the top twenty-two careers in the arts in terms
of the nature of the work, educational or training requirements, getting started, advancement possibilities, salary, employment outlook,
and sources of more information.
    ISBN 0-89434-245-2
    1. Arts--Vocational guidance--United States--Juvenile literature.
[1. Arts--Vocational guidance. 2. Vocational guidance.]
I. J.G. Ferguson Publishing Company.
NX163.C37   1998   97-44034
700'.23'73--dc21   CIP
                                                              AC

Printed in the United States of America

Cover photo courtesy Daniel Aubrey/The Stock Market

Published and distributed by
Ferguson Publishing Company
200 West Madison Street, Suite 300
Chicago, Illinois 60606
312-580-5480

V-2

Table of Contents

Actors

School Subjects
English (writing/literature), Theater/dance.

Personal Interests
Entertaining, Theater

Work Environment
Indoors and outdoors, Primarily multiple locations

Minimum Education Level
High school diploma

Salary Range
$5,000 to $1,000,000+

Certification or Licensing
None

Outlook
Much faster than the average

DOT
150

GOE
01.03.02

NOC
5113

Definition

Actors play parts or roles in dramatic productions on the stage, in motion pictures, or on television or radio. They impersonate, or portray, characters by speech, gesture, song, and dance.

History

Drama was refined as an art form by the ancient Greeks, who used the stage as a forum for topical themes and stories. The role of actors became more important than in the past, and settings became more realistic with the use of scenery. Playgoing was often a great celebration, a tradition carried on by the Romans. The rise of the Christian church put an end to theater in the sixth century CE, and for several centuries actors were ostracized from society, surviving as jugglers and jesters.

Drama was reintroduced during the Middles Ages but became more religious in focus. Plays during this period typically centered around biblical themes, and roles were played by priests and other amateurs. This changed with the rediscovery of Greek and Roman plays in the Renaissance. Professional actors and acting troupes toured the countries of Europe, presenting ancient plays or improvising new dramas based on cultural issues and situations of the day. Actors began to take on more prominence in society. In England, actors such as Will Kemp and Richard Burbage (1567–1619) became known for their roles in the plays of William Shakespeare (1564–1616). In France, Moliere (1622-73) wrote and often acted in his own plays. Until the mid-seventeenth century, however, women were banned from the stage, and the roles of women were played by young boys.

By the eighteenth century, actors could become quite prominent members of society, and plays were often written—or, in the case of Shakespeare's plays, rewritten—to suit a particular actor. Acting styles tended to be highly exaggerated, with elaborate gestures and artificial speech, until David Garrick (1717–79) introduced a more natural style to the stage in the mid-1700s. The first American acting company was established in Williamsburg, Virginia in 1752, led by Lewis Hallan. In the next century, many actors became stars: famous actors of the time included Edwin Forrest (1806–72), Fanny (1809–93) and Charles Kemble, Edmund Kean (1787–1833), William Charles Macready, and Joseph Jefferson (1829–1905), who was particularly well known for his comedic roles.

Until the late nineteenth century, stars dominated the stage. But in 1874, George II, duke of Saxe-Meiningen, formed a theater troupe in which every actor was given equal prominence. This ensemble style influenced others, such as Andre Antoine of France, and gave rise to a new current in theatre called *naturalism,* which featured far more realistic characters in more realistic settings than before. This style of theater came to dominate the twentieth century. It also called for new methods of acting; Konstantin Stanislavsky (1863–1938), of the Moscow Art Theater, developed an especially influential acting style that was later called *method acting,* Stanislavsky influenced the Group Theater in the United States; one member, Lee Strasberg (1901–82), founded the Actors Studio in New York, which would become an important training ground for many of the great American actors. In the early twentieth century, vaudeville and burlesque shows were extremely popular and became the training ground for some of the great comic actors of the century.

By then, developments such as film, radio, and television offered many more acting opportunities than ever before. Many actors honed their skills on the stage and then entered one of these new media, where they could become known throughout the nation and often throughout the world. Both radio and television offered still more acting opportunities in advertisements. The development of sound in film caused many popular actors from the silent era to fade from view, while giving rise to many others. But almost from the beginning, film stars were known for their outrageous salaries and lavish style of living.

In the United States, New York gradually became the center of theater and remains so, although community theater companies abound throughout the country. Hollywood is the recognized center of the motion picture and television industries. Other major production centers are Miami, Chicago, San Francisco, Dallas, and Houston.

Nature of the Work

The imitation or basic development of a character for presentation to an audience often seems like a glamorous and fairly easy job. In reality, it is demanding, tiring work requiring a special talent.

The actor must first find a part available in some upcoming production. This may be in a comedy, drama, musical, or opera. Then, having read and studied the part, the actor must audition before the director and other people who have control of the production. This requirement is often waived for established artists. In film and television, actors must also complete *screen tests,* which are scenes recorded on film, at times performed with other actors, which are later viewed by the director and producer of the film.

If selected for the part, the actor must spend hundreds of hours in rehearsal and must memorize many lines and cues. This is especially true in live theater; in film and television, actors may spend less time in rehearsal and sometimes improvise their lines before the camera, often performing several attempts, or "takes," before the director is satisfied. Actors on television often take advantage of teleprompters, which scroll their lines on a screen in front of them while performing. Radio actors generally read from a script, and therefore rehearsal times are usually shorter.

In addition to such mechanical duties, the actor must determine the essence of the character being portrayed and the relation of that character in the overall scheme of the play. Radio actors must be especially skilled in expressing character and emotion through voice alone. In many film and theater roles, actors must also sing and dance and spend additional time rehearsing songs and perfecting the choreography. Some roles require actors to perform various stunts, which can be quite dangerous. Most often, these stunts are performed by specially trained stuntmen and stuntwomen. Others work as *stand-ins* or *body doubles*. These actors are chosen for specific features and appear on film in place of the lead actor; this is often the case in films requiring nude or seminude scenes. Many television programs, such as game shows, also feature *models,* who generally assist the host of the program.

Actors in the theater may perform the same part many times a week for weeks, months, and sometimes years. This allows them to develop the role, but it can also become tedious. Actors in films may spend several weeks involved in a production, which often takes place on location—that is, in different parts of the world. Television actors involved in a series, such as a soap opera or a situation comedy, also may play the same role for years, generally in thirteen-week cycles. For these actors, however, their lines change from week to week and even from day to day, and much time is spent rehearsing their new lines.

While studying and perfecting their craft, many actors work as *extras,* the nonspeaking characters that people the background on screen or stage. Many actors also continue their training. A great deal of an actor's time is spent attending auditions.

Requirements

There are no minimum educational requirements to become an actor. However, at least a high school diploma is recommended. As acting becomes more and more involved with the various facets of our society, a college degree will become more important to those who hope to have an acting career. It is assumed that the actor who has completed a liberal arts program is more capable of understanding the wide variety of roles that are available. Therefore, it is strongly recommended that aspiring actors complete at least a bachelor's degree program in theater or the dramatic arts. In addition, graduate degrees in the fine arts or in drama are nearly always required should the individual decide to teach dramatic arts.

College can also serve to provide acting experience for the hopeful actor. More than five hundred colleges and universities throughout the country offer dramatic arts programs and present theatrical performances. Actors and directors recommend that those interested in acting gain as much experience as possible through acting in plays in high school and college or in those offered by community groups. Training beyond college is recommended, especially for actors interested in entering the theater. Joining acting workshops, such as the Actors Studio, can often be highly competitive.

Prospective actors will be required not only to have a great talent for acting but also a great determination to succeed in the theater and motion pictures. They must be able to memorize hundreds of lines and should have a good speaking voice. The ability to sing and dance is important for increasing the opportunities for the young actor. Almost every actor, even the biggest stars, are required to audition for a part before they receive the role. In film and television, they will generally complete screen tests to see how they will appear on film. In all fields of acting, a love for acting is a must. It might take many years for an actor to achieve any success, if at all.

Performers on the Broadway stages must be members of the Actors' Equity Association before being cast. While union membership may not always be required, many actors find it advantageous to belong to a union that covers their particular field of performing arts. These organizations include the Actors' Equity Association (stage), Screen Actors Guild or Screen Extras Guild (motion pictures and television films), or American Federation of Television and Radio Artists (television, recording, and radio). In addition, some actors may benefit from membership in the American Guild of Variety Artists (nightclubs, and so on), American Guild of Musical Artists (opera and ballet), or organizations such as the Hebrew Actors Union or Italian Actors Union for productions in those languages.

Opportunities for Experience & Exploration

The best way to explore this career is to participate in school or local theater productions. Even working on the props or lighting crew will provide insight into the field.

Also, attend as many dramatic productions as possible and try to talk with people who either are currently in the theater or have been at one time. They can offer advice to individuals interested in a career in the theater.

Many books, such as *Beginnings,* by Kenneth Branagh, have been written about acting, not only concerning how to perform but also about the nature of the work, its offerings, advantages, and disadvantages.

Methods of Entering

Probably the best way to enter acting is to start with high school, local, or college productions and to gain as much experience as possible on that level. Very rarely is an inexperienced actor given an opportunity to perform on stage or in film in New York or Hollywood. The field is extremely difficult to enter; the more experience and ability beginners have, however, the greater the possibilities for entrance.

Those venturing to New York or Hollywood are encouraged first to have enough money to support themselves during the long waiting and searching period normally required before a job is found. Most will list themselves with a casting agency that will help them find a part as an extra or a bit player, either in theater or film. These agencies keep names on file along with photographs and a description of the individual's features and experience, and if a part comes along that may be suitable, they contact that person. Very often, however, names are added to their lists only when the number of people in a particular physical category is low. For instance, the agency may not have enough athletic young women on their roster, and if the applicant happens to fit this description, her name is added.

Advancement

New actors will normally start in bit parts and will have only a few lines to speak, if any. The normal procession of advancement would then lead to larger supporting roles and then, in the case of theater, possibly to a role as understudy for one of the main actors. The understudy usually has an opportunity to fill in should the main actor be unable to give a performance. Many film and television actors get their start in commercials or by appearing in government and commercially sponsored public service announcements, films, and programs. Other actors join the afternoon soap operas and continue on to evening programs. Many actors have also gotten their start in on-camera roles such as presenting the weather segment of a local news program. Once an actor has gained experience, they may go on to play stronger supporting roles or even leading roles in stage, television, or film productions. From there, an actor may go on to stardom. Only a very small number of actors ever reach that pinnacle, however.

Some actors eventually go into other, related occupations and become *dramatic coaches, drama teachers, producers, stage directors, motion picture directors, television directors, radio directors, stage managers, casting directors,* or *artist and repertoire managers.* Others may combine one or more of these functions while continuing their career as an actor.

Employment Outlook

Motion pictures, television, and the stage are the largest fields of employment for actors, with television commercials representing as much as 60 percent of all acting jobs. Most of the opportunities for employment in these fields are either in Los Angeles or in New York. On stage, even the road shows often have their beginning in New York, with the selection of actors conducted there along with rehearsals. However, nearly every city and most communities present local and regional theater productions.

Jobs in acting are expected to grow much faster than the average through the year 2005. There are a number of factors for this. The growth of cable television in the past decade has created a demand for more actors, especially as the cable networks produce more and more of their own programs and films. The rise of home video has also created new acting jobs, as more and more films are made strictly for the home video market. Many resorts have been created in the 1980s and 1990s, and most present their own theatrical productions, providing more job opportunities for actors. Jobs in theater, however, face pressure as the cost of mounting a production rises and as many nonprofit and smaller theaters lose their funding.

Despite the growth in opportunities, there are many more actors than there are roles, and this is likely to remain true for years to come. This is true in all areas of the arts, including radio, television, motion pictures, and theater, and even those who are employed are normally employed during only a small portion of the year. Many actors must supplement their income by working in other areas, such as secretaries, waiters, or taxi drivers, for example. Almost all performers are members of more than one union in order to take advantage of various opportunities as they become available.

It should be recognized that of the 130,000 or so actors in the United States today, an average of only about 20,000 are employed at any one time. Of these, few are able to support themselves on their earnings from acting, and fewer still will ever achieve stardom. Most actors work for many years before becoming known, and most of these do not rise above supporting roles. The vast majority of actors, meanwhile, are still looking for the right break. There are many more applicants in all areas than there are positions. As with most careers in the arts, people enter this career out of a love and desire for acting.

Earnings

The wage scale for actors is largely controlled through bargaining agreements reached by various unions in negotiations with producers. These agreements normally control the minimum salaries, hours of work permitted per week, and other conditions of employment. The Actors' Equity Association represents actors who work in the theater; the Screen Actors Guild and the Screen Extras Guild represent those who work in motion pictures or film, television, and TV commercials; and the American Federation of Television and Radio Artists represents those who work in television or radio. In addition, each artist enters into a separate contract that may provide for higher salaries.

In the mid-1990s, actors in Broadway productions earn a minimum weekly salary of about $975. Those in smaller productions off-Broadway receive minimums that ranged from $355 to $609 a week depending on the size of the theater. The rate for touring shows is an additional $80 a day.

Motion picture and television minimum rates are $485 daily or $1,685 for a five-day week. Extras earn a minimum of $99 a day. Motion picture actors also receive additional payments known as residuals as part of their guaranteed salary. Many motion picture actors receive residuals whenever films, TV shows, and TV commercials in which they appear are rerun, sold for TV exhibition, or put on videocassette. Residuals often exceed the actors' original salary and account for about one-third of all actors' income.

The annual earnings of persons in television and movies are affected by frequent periods of unemployment. The Actors' Equity Association and the Screen Actors Guild reported that in the 1990s more than 80 percent of their members earned $5,000 or less annually and less than 5 percent earned more than $35,000 from acting. As high as 60 percent of their members had no earnings at all.

In all fields, well-known actors have salary rates above the minimums, and the salaries of the few top stars are many times higher. Actors in television series may earn tens of thousands of dollars per week, while a few may earn as much as $1 million or more per week. Salaries for these actors vary considerably and are negotiated individually. In film, top stars may earn as much as $20 million per film, and, after receiving a percentage of the gross earned by the film, these stars can earn far, far more. Until recent years, female film stars tended to earn lower salaries than their male counterparts; the emergence of stars such as Demi Moore and others has started to reverse that trend. The average annual earnings for all motion picture actors, however, are usually low (only $12,000 for screen actors in the 1990s) for all but the best-known performers because of the periods of unemployment.

Conditions of Work

Actors work under varying conditions. Those employed in motion pictures may work in air-conditioned studios one week and be on location in a hot desert the next.

Those in stage productions perform under all types of conditions. The number of hours employed per day or week vary, as do the number of weeks employed per year. Stage actors normally perform eight shows per week with any additional performances paid for as overtime. The basic work week after the show opens is about thirty-six hours unless major changes in the play are needed. The number of hours worked per week is considerably more before the opening, because of rehearsals. Evening work is a natural part of a stage actor's life. Rehearsals often are held at night and over holidays and weekends. If the play goes on the road, much traveling will be involved.

A number of actors cannot receive unemployment compensation when they are waiting for their next part, primarily because they have not worked enough to meet the minimum eligibility requirements for compensation. Sick leaves and paid vacations are not usually available to the actor. However, union actors who earn the minimum qualifications now receive full medical and health insurance under all the actors' unions. Those who earn health plan benefits for ten years become eligible for a pension upon retirement. The acting field is very uncertain. Aspirants never know whether they will be able to get into the profession, and, once in, there are uncertainties as to whether the show will be well received and, if not, whether the actors' talent can survive a bad show.

Sources of Additional Information

Actors' Equity Association
165 West 46th Street
New York, NY 10036
Tel: 212-869-8530

American Federation of Television and Radio Artists
260 Madison Avenue
New York, NY 10016
Tel: 212-532-0800

American Guild of Musical Artists
1727 Broadway
New York, NY 10019
Tel: 212-265-3687

American Guild of Variety Artists
184 Fifth Avenue
New York, NY 10019
Tel: 212-675-1003

Associated Actors and Artists of America (AFL-CIO)
165 West 46th Street
New York, NY 10036
Tel: 212-869-0358

National Association of Schools of Theater
11250 Roger Bacon Drive, Suite 21
Reston, VA 22090
Tel: 703-437-0700

Actors

- **Screen Actors Guild**
  7065 Hollywood Boulevard
  Hollywood, CA 90028
  Tel: 213-549-6400

- **Screen Extras Guild**
  3253 North Knoll Drive
  Los Angeles, CA 90068-1517
  Tel: 213-851-4301

Camera Operators

Definition

Motion picture camera operators use motion picture cameras and equipment to photograph subjects or material for movies, television programs, or commercials. They usually use 35-millimeter or 16-millimeter cameras or camcorders and a variety of films, lenses, tripods, and filters in their work. Their instructions usually come from *cinematographers* or *directors of photography*. Camera operators are also known as *cameramen.*

History

Motion pictures were made as early as 1877, using a series of still photographs to create the illusion of motion. But it was Thomas A. Edison who, in 1889, produced the first single-unit motion picture camera that set the standard for today.

The motion picture industry blossomed in the United States during the twentieth century. With the growth of the television industry and the addition of commercial advertising to television, camera operators became indispensable members of the production crew. Motion picture directors and producers rely on camera operators to create the images on film that the directors and producers envision in their minds. As camera equipment becomes more complex and sophisticated, the camera operator will need to be more proficient at his or her craft.

Nature of the Work

Motion picture camera operators may work on feature films in Hollywood or on location elsewhere. Many work on educational films, documentaries, or television programs. The nature of the camera operator's work depends largely on the size of the production crew. If the film is a documentary or short news segment, the camera operator may be responsible for setting up the camera and lighting equipment as well as for supervising the actors during filming. Equipment that camera operators typically use can include cranes, dollies, mounting heads, and different types of lenses and accessories. Often the camera operator is also responsible for maintenance and repair of all of this equipment.

With a larger crew, the camera operator is responsible only for the actual filming. The camera operator may even have a support team of assistants. The *first assistant camera operator* will typically focus the cameras, make sure cameras are loaded, and confer with lighting specialists. In larger productions, there are also backup cameras and accessories for use if one should malfunction during filming. *Second assistant camera operators* help the first assistant set up scenes to be filmed and assist in the maintenance of the equipment.

Sometimes camera operators must use shoulder-held cameras. This often occurs during the filming of action scenes for television or motion pictures. *Special effects*, or *optical effects camera operators*, photograph the special effects segments for motion pictures and television. They create illusions or effects that can add mood and tone to the motion picture. They usually add fades, dissolves, superimpositions, and other effects to their films at the request of the director of photography.

Requirements

A college degree is not necessary to get a position as a motion picture camera operator. Most camera operators learn on the job. Many colleges and film schools do offer training in camera operation and cinematography, but actual experience as a camera operator is the best guarantee of consistent employment. Camera operators must be able to work closely with other members of a film crew, and they must understand how their own equipment works. Since lighting is an integral part of filmmaking, camera operators should have a thorough understanding of lighting equipment as well.

Opportunities for Experience & Exploration

Students interested in careers as camera operators should join photography clubs. They can also learn about photography by working in a camera shop. A part-time job in a camera shop gives a student a basic understanding of photographic equipment. Some school districts have television stations where students can learn the basics of camera operation. This kind of hands-on experience is invaluable when it comes time to find work in the field.

The American Society of Cinematographers publishes a monthly magazine, *American Cinematographer.* The book *TV Careers Behind the Screen,* published in 1987 by John Wiley and Sons, has a chapter on the camera operator.

Schools for performing arts, universities, and all branches of the military offer training in cinematography. Courses in photography are often offered as part of a communications or journalism program. They teach the basics of photographic equipment, techniques, and processes. The best preparation for a career as a camera operator, however, is an apprenticeship. Working in a studio for a camera operator, cinematographer, or director of photography gives a potential camera operator the best idea of what the work is like.

Methods of Entering

Most entry-level jobs require little formal preparation in photography or camera operation. A college degree is not required by most film or television studios. An entry-level job as a cinematography assistant usually begins with assignments such as setting up or loading film into cameras and adjusting or checking lighting. With experience, the assistant may participate in decisions about what to photograph or how to film a particular scene.

Advancement

It usually takes two to four years for a motion picture camera operator to learn the techniques necessary for the job. Those who become proficient in their field can move up to become director of photography, or cinematographer. It takes from four to ten years to reach this level. The *cinematographer,* or director of photography, supervises other camera operators, and works more closely with the directors, producers, and actors in the creation of the film. Some camera operators study cinematography part-time while keeping their jobs as camera operators. They may later move to larger studios or command higher salaries.

Employment Outlook

The outlook for motion picture camera operators is very favorable for all occupations through the year 2005. The use of visual images continues to grow in areas such as communication, education, entertainment, marketing, and research and development. More businesses will make use of video training films and public relations projects that use film. The entertainment industries are also expanding. However, competition for positions is very fierce. Camera operators work in what is considered a desirable and exciting field, and they must work hard and be aggressive to get good jobs, especially in Los Angeles and New York.

Earnings

Typically, camera operators working on a motion picture get paid on a per-day basis. Their role in the creation of the movie may last several weeks, or several months. Yet it is rare that a camera operator works twelve months out of the year.

Many camera operators belong to the International Photographers Union. The union sets minimum per-day wage scales for camera operators working on motion pictures and television broadcasts. The union has set the following minimum wage scales based upon an eight-hour work day: director of photography, $508; camera operator, $310; first assistant camera operator, $225; second assistant camera operator, $207; *film loader,* $176. Most camera operators with experience negotiate higher fees for their service filming a motion picture. An established and experienced director of photography, for example, can earn as much as $10,000 per week.

Conditions
of Work

Motion picture camera operators work indoors and outdoors. Most work for motion picture studios or in television broadcasting. During filming, a camera operator may spend several weeks or months on location in another city or country. Most often the camera operator lives at home and comes to work during regular business hours. Hours can be erratic, however, if the film includes scenes that must be shot at night, or if a deadline must be met by after-hours filming.

Much of the work of a camera operator becomes routine after a few years of experience. Camera operators get used to loading and unloading film, carrying cameras and equipment from trucks or workshops into studios or sets, and filming segments over and over again. The glamour of working on motion pictures or television programs may be diminished by the physically demanding work. Also, the actors, directors, and producers are in the limelight. They often receive credit for the work the camera operators have done.

Many camera operators must be available on short notice. Since motion picture camera operators are generally hired to work on one film at a time, there may be long periods during which a camera operator is not working. Few can make a living as self-employed camera operators.

Motion picture camera operators working on documentary or news productions may work in dangerous places. Sometimes they must work in uncomfortable positions or make adjustments for imperfect lighting conditions. They usually operate their cameras while standing hours at a time. Deadline pressure is also a constant in the camera operator's work. Working for directors or producers who are on tight budgets or strict schedules may be very stressful.

Sources of Additional Information

■ **American Society of TV Cameramen**
4314 Hilary Street
Las Vegas, NV 89117
Tel: 702-228-6704

■ **International Alliance of Theatrical Stage Employees and Moving Picture Machine Operators**
1515 Broadway
New York, NY 10036
Tel: 212-730-1770

Camera Operators

■ **Society of Motion Picture and Television Engineers**
595 West Hartsdale Avenue
White Plains, NY 10607
Tel: 914-761-1100
Email: eng@smpte.org

Cartoonists and Animators

School Subjects
Art, English (writing/literature)

Personal Interests
Drawing/painting, Film and Television

Work Environment
Primarily indoors, Primarily one location

Minimum Education Level
Some postsecondary training

Salary Range
$200 per week to $1,500+ per week

Certification or Licensing
None

Outlook
About as fast as the average

DOT
141

GOE
01.02.03

NOC
5241

Definition

Cartoonists and *animators* are illustrators who draw pictures and cartoons to amuse, educate, and persuade people.

History

Cartoons and animation have become commonplace in the twentieth century. Cartoons appear in the editorial and funny pages of daily newspapers, in comic books, textbooks, and magazines, in movie theaters, children's television, and commercials. Many cartoon characters have become household names, such as Little Orphan Annie, Superman, and Charlie Brown. Some comic strips create fantasy worlds for their readers to escape to; others, such as Walt Kelly's (1913–1973) *Pogo* and Garry Trudeau's (born 1948)

Doonesbury, are so relevant to the real world that their readers may often refer to them rather than the evening news to learn about current events.

Animation, a specialization of cartooning, has come to the forefront over its parent art, due largely to Walt Disney. Currently popular in animated movies is the live-action feature, for example, *Who Framed Roger Rabbit?*, in which human actors interact with cartoon characters to stunning effect. Computer technology has become vital to animation, facilitating the production of animated films and special effects. Because of the many applications of their work, cartoonists and animators have become busy and popular artists.

Nature of the Work

Cartoonists draw illustrations for newspapers, books, magazines, greeting cards, movies, television shows, civic organizations, and private businesses. Cartoons most often are associated with newspaper comics or with children's television, but they are also used to highlight and interpret information in publications as well as in advertising.

Whatever their individual specialty, cartoonists and animators translate ideas onto paper or film in order to communicate these ideas to an audience. Sometimes the ideas are original; other times they are directly related to the news of the day, to the content of a magazine article, or to a new product. After cartoonists come up with ideas, they discuss them with their employers, who include editors, producers, and creative directors at advertising agencies. Next, cartoonists sketch drawings and submit these for approval. Employers may suggest changes, which cartoonists then make. Cartoonists use a variety of art materials including pens, pencils, markers, crayons, paints, transparent washes, and shading sheets. They may draw on paper, acetate, or bristol board.

Animators are relying increasingly on computers in various areas of production. They are used to color animation art, where every frame used to be painted by hand. They are also used to create special effects or even entire films.

Editorial cartoonists comment on society by drawing pictures with messages that are usually funny, but which often have a satirical edge. Their drawings often depict famous politicians. *Portraitists* are cartoonists who specialize in drawing caricatures. Caricatures are pictures that exaggerate someone's prominent features, such as a large nose, to make them recognizable to the public. Most editorial cartoonists are also talented portraitists.

Requirements

Cartoonists and animators must be creative. In addition to having artistic talent, they must generate ideas, although it is not unusual for cartoonists to collaborate with writers for ideas. Whether they create cartoon strips or advertising campaigns, they must be able to come up with concepts and images that the public will respond to. They must have a good sense of humor and an observant eye to detect people's distinguishing characteristics and society's interesting attributes or incongruities.

Cartoonists and animators need not have a college degree, but some art training is usually expected by employers. To comment insightfully on contemporary life, it is also useful to study political science, history, and social studies. Animators must attend art school to learn specific technical skills. Training in computers in addition to art can be especially valuable. Cartoonists and animators need to be flexible. Because their art is commercial, they must be willing to accommodate their employers' desires if they are to build a broad clientele and earn a decent living. They must be able to take suggestions and rejections gracefully.

Opportunities for Experience & Exploration

High school students who are interested in becoming cartoonists or animators should submit their drawings to their school paper. They also might want to draw posters to publicize activities, such as sporting events, dances, and meetings.

Scholarship assistance for art students is available from various sources. For example, the Society of Illustrators awards around 125 scholarships annually to artist students from any field. Students do not apply directly; rather, they are selected and given application materials by their instructors. The International Animated Film Society offers scholarships to high school seniors.

Methods of Entering

A few places, such as the Walt Disney studios, offer apprenticeships. To enter these programs, applicants must have attended an accredited art school for two or three years.

Formal entry-level positions for cartoonists and animators are rare, but there are several ways for artists to enter the cartooning field. Most cartoonists and animators begin by working piecemeal, selling cartoons to small publications, like community newspapers, that buy freelance cartoons. Others assemble a portfolio of their best work and apply to publishers or the art departments of advertising agencies. Cartoonists and animators should be willing to work for what equals less than minimum wage to get established.

Advancement

Cartoonists' success, like that of other artists, depends upon how much the public likes their work. Very successful cartoonists and animators work for prestigious clients at the best wages; some become well known to the public.

Employment Outlook

Job opportunities for cartoonists and animators are expected to grow faster than average through the year 2000, but competition for both salaried and freelance cartooning jobs is keen. Almost two-thirds of all visual artists are self-employed, but freelance work can be hard to come by and many freelancers earn little until they acquire experience and establish a good reputation.

Earnings

Freelance cartoonists may earn anywhere from $100 to $1,200 or more per drawing, but top dollar generally goes only for big, full-color projects such as magazine cover illustrations. Most cartoonists and animators average from $200 to $1,500 a week, although syndicated cartoonists on commission can earn much more. Salaries depend upon the work performed; a key artist such as an animator can expect to earn around $1,000 per week, a cell painter $800, and a production worker $400. Comic strip artists are usually paid according to the number of publications that carry their strip. Self-employed artists do not receive fringe benefits such as paid vacations, sick leave, health insurance, or pension benefits.

Conditions of Work

Most cartoonists and animators work in big cities where employers such as television studios, magazine publishers, and advertising agencies are located. They generally work in comfortable environments, at drafting tables or drawing boards with good lighting. Staff cartoonists work a regular forty-hour week, but may occasionally be expected to work evenings and weekends to meet deadlines. Freelance cartoonists have erratic schedules, and the number of hours they work may depend on how much money they want to earn or how much work they can find. They often work evenings and weekends, but are not required to be at work during regular office hours.

Cartoonists and animators can be frustrated by employers who curtail their creativity, asking them to follow instructions that are contrary to what they would most like to do. Many freelance cartoonists spend a lot of time working alone at home, but cartoonists have more opportunities to interact with other people than most working artists.

Sources of Additional Information

For membership and scholarship information, contact:

▪ **International Animated Film Society**
725 South Victory
Burbank, CA 91502
Tel: 818-842-8330

For education and career information, please contact:

▪ **National Cartoonists Society**
PO Box 20267
Columbus Circle Station
New York, NY 10023
Tel: 212-627-1550

For an art school directory, a scholarship guide, or general information, please contact:

▪ **National Art Education Association**
1916 Association Drive
Reston, VA 22091-1590
Tel: 703-860-8000

For scholarship information for qualified students in art school, have your instructor contact:

▪ **Society of Illustrators**
128 East 63rd Street
New York, NY 10021
Tel: 212-838-2560

Ceramic Artists

School Subjects
Archeology, Art

Personal Interests
Drawing/painting, Sculpting

Work Environment
Indoors and outdoors, Primarily one location

Minimum Education Level
Some postsecondary training

Salary Range
$15,000 to $100,000

Certification or Licensing
Recommended

Outlook
Little change or more slowly than the average

DOT
779

GOE
01.06.02

NOC
5244

Definition

Ceramic artists—also known as *potters, ceramists, sculptors,* and *clay artists*—work with clay to make both functional and purely aesthetic objects. They blend basic elements (such as clay and water) and more specialized components (such as texture fillers, colorants, and talc) and form the mixture into shapes; they then use glazing and firing techniques to finish their pieces. Depending on the artist's individual inclinations, they use either manual techniques or wheel throwing techniques to create such things as functional pottery (like coffee cups and vases), beads, tiles, architectural installations, and sculptures.

History

Ceramic artists today are part of a historic tradition twelve thousand years old that involves using clay to create form and beauty. According to Kentucky potter Gwen Heffner, two things constant throughout all recorded history have compelled the making and use of pottery: "the continuing ritual use of containers for food and sustenance, and the desire and search for beauty. People still need a bowl, cup, or plate to eat from. In a world that struggles with its barbarity, humans have an even greater need for serenity and beauty."

The word *ceramics* is from the Greek word *keramos,* meaning "potter's clay and ware." Ceramic artistry has always involved the basic method of making clay products permanent by applying heat. The oldest known ceramic objects are from the Near East; these are small models of figures probably used in spiritual ceremonies around 10,000 BCE. The early knowledge of using fire to harden damp clay into ceramic material became widespread about 6000 to 4000 BCE and afterward the craft of ceramics developed differently in various areas of the world.

As generations of humans evolved, the technique of building up pots with coils eventually developed into the use of some kind of turntable to make it easier to shape the clay into vessel forms. One of the earliest pottery-turning devices found is believed to have been used by a potter in ancient Ur about 3500 BCE. Although it is not known precisely when it happened, at some point afterward the simple stone turntable evolved into a true potter's wheel. This technological development was so important that the Egyptians believed a god had invented the potter's wheel.

Whatever techniques or tools were used to shape early clay objects, all pieces had to be treated by heat to become hardened, permanent ceramics. The earliest method involved heating objects in open fire pits, often also burning straw inside the pottery to dry and warm them. By about 3000 BCE, in the region now known as Israel, potters were building enclosed kilns; in China, kilns were being made that had tunnels leading to beehive-shaped chambers, thus creating forced drafts and improved use of fuel; and in Mesopotamia, kilns had domed roofs and perforated floors. Using kilns, potters came to have more control over the fire, and wind was less of a problem than when open firing methods were used.

Today's ceramic artists continue to use modern adaptations of the early potter's wheel when they are making such container vessels as pots, cups, and vases. For making functional pottery, what has always mattered is the emptiness that is created when a pot is "thrown on the wheel"; the hole becomes just as important as the shape of the pottery itself. Modern artists also use adaptations of early firing methods (although old methods of open firing are still used today in certain villages in Fiji, Africa, the Middle East, and the southwestern United

States). But today's ceramics technology—including the use of knowledge based on chemistry; space-age kiln insulation; and computer-controlled kilns—provides artists so many more techniques and tools with which to work their craft. The vision of today's ceramic artist can be considered much wider than that of the ancient sculptor of fertility figurines.

Many pottery companies began to produce "art pottery" around the turn of the century, and this was influenced by art movements in the United States and Europe. For example, at the Rookwood Pottery in Cincinnati, Ohio, artists designed and produced Standard Ware, which eventually became quite popular. Adelaine Alsop Robineau (1865–1929) cast her own ware and learned to throw her forms on the wheel; she often worked for hundreds of hours on individual pieces, carving intricate designs and raised patterns. George Ohr was an innovative potter of the early 1900s who made vases and pots that expressed his unique personality (one set of his glazed earthenware is titled "Six O'Clock in the Evening" and "Three O'Clock in the Morning"). Rookwood Pottery, Robineau, and Ohr are just three representatives of the ceramic artistry that led to what is being expressed today. The U.S. architect Louis Sullivan influenced architectural ceramics by using clay to ornament his metal-framed buildings; the Moravian Pottery and Tile Works (Pennsylvania) influenced the tile making niche and is still producing tiles today; and the work of artists such as Maija Grotell, Laura Anderson, Bernard Leach, and Shoji Hamada continue to influence students in the ceramic arts.

Artists continue to make such simple works as delicate porcelain vases, but they also experiment and explore diverse forms like performance work, large architectural creations, odd-shaped sculptural vessels, and environmental installations. The artist's vision has new sources of imagery (history, mythology, social concern, autobiography) with which to work, all leading, however, back to hands working with clay.

Nature of the Work

The ceramic artist uses clay like the painter uses paint, like the musician uses sound, like the dancer uses movement. If one is considered an artist, the work one does is often not considered a "job." The artist understands clay and its properties and has chosen it as a medium to create visual expressions of ideas, feelings, concepts, and concerns. Ceramic artist Harvey Sadow says of his work: "It is possible for an artist to empower an object with a spirit capable of ringing the bells of understanding or triggering sacred memories. Art then becomes a vehicle of transport to the quiet place where revelation begins again, as it did in childhood."

The particular properties of clay influence artists' decisions about what they are going to make—be it functional or purely aesthetic—and how they are going to make it. For some ceramic artists, shape and form are all-important. For others, throwing on the wheel is what matters most. In any case, clay is the basis. But what is clay? Where does it come from? How does it become a work of art?

Clay is found beneath rich topsoil and often under layers of rock. Weather conditions—rain, snow, wind—wear down the earth's rock surface, causing it to decompose and become primary clay. The action of water also moves earth particles and deposits them elsewhere, forming beds of secondary clay. Different types of clay—like ball clay, earthenware clay, and stoneware clay—are dug from such deposits and can then be transformed by the ceramic artist. If you hold a lump of damp clay in your hands, you'll feel its softness and pliability. To become hard and permanent after shaping, each type of clay needs to be fired to a certain temperature in an open fire or a kiln. The variations in the size of the clay particles and the different temperatures at which clays reach their maturity (correct hardness) produce the differences in texture and appearance among different pieces. For instance, earthenware clay is fired at low temperatures and does not become as dense as clays like porcelain and stoneware, which are fired at higher temperatures.

Although each artist works the clay in a unique way, there are some basic methods that can be used to define the nature of an artist's work. Some ceramic artists build their objects almost completely by hand, not using a potter's wheel; others use a wheel to mold their forms; others make molds and pour clay into them. Handbuilding allows a potter to build free-form art, while the potter's wheel aids in making symmetrically shaped works. In both cases, one must prepare the clay by wedging, which involves throwing the clay body down hard against a flat surface or simply kneading it. Wedging removes the bubbles and provides a consistent level of moisture throughout the clay.

In handbuilding, an artist uses either the coil or the slab method. The coil method entails forming long rods of clay, coiling the rods into a desired shape, and blending the coils to create a smooth surface. With slabs, one simply joins pieces of clay together to make a pot or other shape. Before actually joining the slabs or coiling, the artist must score the adjoining edges-that is, lightly nick them to create a rough surface-and add watery clay known as slip. This process helps the clay pieces stick together.

When using a potter's wheel, one places a wedged piece of clay in the middle of the wheel, centers the clay body so that a symmetrical shape can be formed, and pushes down the center of the solid clay body to begin forming walls. Shaping a pot involves skilled hand movements that cause the clay to bend and constrict as desired.

Once a pot is taken off the wheel, it is left to dry until it is leather hard. At that time, the artist places the clay body back on the wheel to trim off any uneven edges and form a base. The artist can paint the body or apply slip to add texture at this point. When the body is bone dry, it is placed into an open fire or a kiln for several hours. Afterward, the artist applies glaze and fires the body again.

Pouring clay into a mold and throwing it on a wheel is called jig-gering; mass-produced objects like sinks and jars are often made this way. But many potters and sculptors create single objects by pressing or pouring clay into molds without using the wheel. They use hump molds (any material over which you can press clay), plaster press molds, polystyrene foam molds, or other creative types of molds (one artist used a shark's head; another used a motorcycle guard).

Some would say that there are only fine lines that distinguish the different types of ceramic artists from each other. Who is the potter? the sculptor? Who would rather consider herself a clay artist? Basically, ceramic artists are defined by the objects they make and usually by whether the objects are functional or statements of the particular artist's creativity and vision.

The term *production potter* usually refers to a ceramic artist who makes a full series of household ware. The production potter also often makes what is called studio pottery—vases, bowls, and other pieces made more for display than for everyday use. These potters might work alone in a studio or with one or two colleagues or helpers, or they might set up a large workshop employing several people.

Other artists concentrate on specific niches in which they enjoy producing objects considered both functional and artful. Or one might go through phases, working as a potter for a while, then sculpt-ing, then exploring other creative inclinations. Bead making, tile making, and making architectural ceramics are a few examples of creative endeavors. *Architectural ceramists* work on such things as tile-decorated subway stations, ceramic-clad building columns, and other types of sculptural installations in public settings like muse-ums, shopping malls, and parks.

The *ceramic sculptor* is one who is more inclined to create works of art rather than functional pottery. Using clay and often other types of art media, sculptors handbuild more than they throw on the wheel. They begin with some influence on their imagination and, like painters using gesso and canvas, they follow a creative journey that ends with a sculpture of limitless proportions. The shapes, sizes, and images of these works of art represent each artist's own ego, creative process, imagination, and skill. For example, one artist made a life-size sculpture of a seated man and installed it in a cafe, where he sits either alone or as part of a group of customers; another artist created dozens of sculptured molds of her forehead and installed them in her house as part of a "library of thought." Such individuality is key to the artist's vision and work.

Many artists feel that their goals lie in simply being able to work at their art, in whatever environment. They might not be especially concerned about whether their pieces sell to the public; they might be more satisfied to know that a limited group of people enjoy their work. Others want specifically to have their own studios, produce many pieces, and become famous in the art world. It depends on your own desires, your own personality, your own concern with what brings fulfillment in your life's work.

Employment Outlook

It is very hard to predict whether ceramic artists will enjoy success and recognition in the near future. Within the broader art world—which includes painting, architecture, and sculpture—ceramic art and design is quite new. Ceramics instruction is widespread today, but as late as the 1930s it wasn't really considered much of an art. People today still debate whether it is a craft or an art.

However, there are good signs that ceramics as an art form has the potential to become well recognized. The 1990s have produced many books, videos, and magazines on the subject, along with workshops, conferences, and competitions throughout the world. Ceramic artists gather to show their work, work together, and teach others. Many have made names for themselves in the art world and are valued as artists.

Earnings

To most artists, earnings come in different forms, not just monetary wealth. Of course many would like to be successful in terms of how many pieces they sell and how much money they make, but this doesn't happen with every ceramic artist. One might work hundreds of hours on one piece of sculpture, finally realizing that he or she doesn't want to part with it at all. Another might be tremendously inspired, quickly throw an unusually good pot on the wheel, and immediately offer it for sale.

If you want to earn steady pay, it would be wise to work for an established potter or a large ceramics manufacturer. This type of job might pay at least $15,000 to $25,000 per year, and you'll get a paycheck every few weeks. For many, being an artist is more satisfying than having a good income. Setting up one's own studio, being able to get involved in the creative process whenever inspiration strikes, working with clay—this type of living is what many artists strive for. Don't forget, though, that if you work for yourself you won't have a company looking out for your health insurance, paid vacations, and other fringe benefits that come with regular full-time positions.

Conditions of Work

Living the life of an artist can be hugely reward-ing, fulfilling, and enlightening. For all ceramic artists, the creative process must be an elemental part of their existence. Whether you are a functional potter, a sculptor, or a tile maker, this creative process is the most significant condition of your work.

The life of a professional ceramic artist is like that of other artists— the work is personally rewarding but perhaps difficult, with earned money and recognition often out of proportion to the training, time, and effort involved. Perhaps the most difficult task for the potter wanting his or her own studio is to be practical. You must consider costs for such things as the clay, kiln, fuel, chemicals, and the rental of studio space and utilities.

Your work space might be a studio at school, a potter's workshop, or your basement or garage. An artist's work area often reflects the activity done there, the personality of the artist, and the techniques used to create the ceramic pieces. Your studio space doesn't have to be elaborate, but certain things—like spaciousness, ventilation, and lighting—should be considered. Health and safety issues should be considered as well; a studio should have a filter vacuum cleaner, venting system, and fire extinguisher.

Sources of Additional Information

For general information on ceramic arts study, contact:

■ **National Art Education Association**
1916 Association Drive
Reston, VA 22091
Tel: 703-860-8000

■ **National Council on Education for the Ceramic Arts**
PO Box 1677
Bandon, OR 97411
Tel: 503-347-4394

For information on a scholarship offered for a specific summer workshop in Maine, contact:

■ **Haystack Mountain School of Crafts**
Deer Isle, ME 04627
Tel: 207-348-2306

Cinematographers and Directors of Photography

School Subjects
Art, English (writing/literature)

Personal Interests
Film and Television, Photography

Work Environment
Indoors and outdoors, Primarily multiple locations

Minimum Education Level
Bachelor's degree

Salary Range
$5,000 to $780,000

Certification or Licensing
None

Outlook
Little change or more slowly than the average

DOT
143

GOE
10.02.03

NOC
5131

Definition

The *director of photography,* also called the *cinematographer,* is instrumental in establishing the mood of a film, using every technical device at his or her disposal. The primary tool is the camera; the director of photography (DP) is responsible for every shot's framing, lighting, color level, and exposure—elements that set the artistic tone of the film. The DP works with the director to translate a written script into an artistic product.

History

Motion picture cameras were invented in the late 1800s. In 1903 Edwin Porter made *The Great Train Robbery,* the first motion picture that used modern filmmakers' techniques to tell a story. Porter filmed the scenes out of sequence, then edited and spliced them together to make the film, as is done today.

In the early years of film, the director handled the camera and made the artistic decisions that today are the job of the director of photography. The technical sophistication and artistic choices that are part of today's filming process had not yet emerged—directors merely filmed narratives without moving the camera. Lighting was more for functional purposes of illumination than for artistic effect. Soon, however, directors began to experiment; they moved the camera to shoot from different angles and established a variety of editing techniques.

In the 1950s the dominance of major studios in film production was curbed by an antitrust court decision, and more independent films were made. Changes in the United States tax code made independent producing more profitable. New genres and trends challenged the director and artistic staff of a production; science fiction, adventure, mystery, and romance could all be attained according to a variety of artistic decisions made by the director with the director of photography. By the late 1970s university film schools were established, training students in directing and cinematography as well as in other areas.

Nature of the Work

The director of photography is a prestigious position for a person with both artistic and technical knowledge. There are DPs in both film and television who work with the director to interpret a script and bring it to life.

The work of the DP begins with reading the script and talking to the director about how to film each scene. Together they determine how to achieve the desired effects by deciding on camera angles and movement, lighting, framing, and the filters they will use. By manipulating effects they will determine the mood of a scene; for example, to raise the level of tension and discomfort in an argument, the camera can film at an unusual angle or move around the actors as they speak. The director may film a scene in more than one way and then choose which best suits the project. With good collaboration between the director and the DP, decisions will be made quickly and successfully.

The DP is responsible for assembling the camera crew and telling them how to film each scene. He or she must be knowledgeable about all aspects of camera operation, lighting, filters, and types of film. There are multiple ways an effect can be approached, and a DP must be aware of them in order to make suggestions to the director and to capture the mood desired. For small, low-budget films, some of the crew's roles may be combined; for example, the DP may operate a camera in addition to overseeing the crew.

In a large production, the crew's roles will be more specialized. The *camera operator* either operates the camera physically or controls it remotely, using a control panel. The *first assistant camera operator* helps with focus, changes lenses and filters, sets the stop for film exposure, and makes sure the camera is working properly. Focus is extremely important and is not entrusted to vision; the first assistant carries a measuring tape and measures all the key positions of the actors to ensure correct focus. The *second assistant camera operator,* also called the *loader,* loads film magazines, keeps track of how much film stock is left, and keeps camera reports. Camera reports record which shots the director likes and wants to have printed. The DP also is in charge of the *gaffer,* who leads the electrical crew, and the *grips,* who handle the dollies and cranes to move the cameras.

When shooting begins, the director of photography will take a series of test shots of film locations to determine the lighting, lenses, and film stock that will work best. Once filming starts, the DP will make adjustments as necessary. He or she may also film screen tests of actors so the director can be sure they are right for their parts.

Advances in technology have opened new possibilities in filming. Whereas crane arms used to have to support a camera and two or more people, now a camera can be operated remotely, so it can move quickly and easily through the air on a magnesium pole. Helicopter mounts allow for spectacular shots from the air. The DP must keep on top of changes in technology and equipment to make these techniques available to the director.

Quality and consistency of shooting are extremely important. If there are any inconsistencies resulting from a camera crew using the wrong filter or film, for example, the audience will notice. Often a scene will be filmed with several cameras in different positions, perhaps over the course of one or more days, but the light quality and camera positions must remain consistent.

Requirements

A bachelor's degree in liberal arts or film studies provides a good background for work in the film industry. Film school can be especially useful for those who wish to advance to the position of director of photography. There are more than five hundred film studies programs at colleges and universities throughout the United States, including those considered to be the five most reputable: the American Film Institute (Los Angeles, CA), Columbia University (New York, NY), New York University, the University of California at Los Angeles (UCLA), and the University of Southern California (USC). These schools have film professionals on their faculties and provide a very visible stage for student talent, being located in the two film business hot spots—California and New York. (The tuition for film programs offered elsewhere, however, tends to be much less expensive than at these schools.)

Film school offers overall formal training, providing an education in fundamental skills by working with student productions. Such education is rigorous, but in addition to teaching skills it provides aspiring industry professionals with peer groups and a network of contacts with students, faculty, and guest speakers that can be of help after graduation.

The director of photography should keep abreast of technological innovations. He or she must be comfortable with the technical as well as artistic aspects of the profession.

A good DP must be able to work well with other people. Since the director has final say over the artistic choices in a film, the DP must bend when their opinions differ. The DP must be a good leader, able to choose and direct his or her crew effectively.

Opportunities for Experience & Exploration

Visit libraries and bookstores to read more about the field. Browse magazine racks to find trade magazines and other related material on your area of interest; *American Cinematographer* will be particularly useful, and *Daily Variety* and *Hollywood Reporter* are also good sources to consult.

Since experience and jobs are difficult to get in the film and television industry, it is important to learn about the career to be sure it is right for you. Look for volunteer work experience at film and local television studios or with independent filmmakers, who rely on volunteers to defray expenses.

Methods of Entering

Internships are a very good way to gain experience and make yourself a marketable job candidate. Since local television stations and lower-budget film productions operate with limited funds, they may offer internships for course credit or experience instead of a salary.

Camera operators may choose to join a union; some film studios will only hire union members. The principal union for this field is the International Alliance of Theatrical Stage Employees and Moving Picture Machine Operators of the United States and Canada (IATSE). Union members work under a union contract that determines their work rules, pay, and benefits.

Advancement

Once you have reached the career of director of photography, you are at the top of the ladder for this field. At this point it is important to build a reputation, since a respected DP will get more prestigious projects and be able to accept jobs that seem particularly interesting or challenging.

Employment Outlook

Film and television are popular industries; thus, even though they have grown in recent years, competition is stiff for positions.

Earnings

Salaries vary largely depending upon a DP's experience and reputation; a beginning DP may earn $420 a day, while one with substantial experience can earn $15,000 a week.

Conditions of Work

Conditions of work will vary, since the DP will often be on the set. In television production and in movies, this may be indoors or outdoors. Hours can be long, and the shooting schedule rigorous, especially when a film is going over budget.

Sources of Additional Information

■ **Academy of Motion Picture Arts and Sciences**
8949 Wilshire Boulevard
Beverly Hills, CA 90211
Tel: 310-247-3000
WWW: http://www.lightside.com/ampas/

For information about colleges with film and television programs of study, please contact:

▄ **American Film Institute**
PO Box 27999
2021 North Western Avenue
Los Angeles, CA 90027
Tel: 213-856-7600
WWW: http://www.afionline.org

Comedians

School Subjects
English (writing/literature), Theater/dance

Personal Interests
Entertaining, Writing

Work Environment
Primarily indoors, Primarily multiple locations

Minimum Education Level
High school diploma

Salary Range
$6,000 to $200,000+

Certification or Licensing
None

Outlook
About as fast as the average

DOT
159

GOE
01.03.02

NOC
5232

Definition

Comedians are entertainers who make people laugh. They use a variety of techniques to amuse their audiences, including telling jokes, composing and singing humorous songs, wearing funny costumes, and doing impersonations. Comedians perform in nightclubs, comedy clubs, coffee houses, theaters, television shows, films, and even business functions, such as trade shows and sales meetings.

History

Throughout history, people have enjoyed humorous interpretations of the events that make up their daily lives. Comedy began as a type of drama that presented events in a comic way and thereby sought to amuse its audience. These dramas were not always funny, yet they were usually lighthearted and had happy endings (as opposed to tragedies, which had sad endings).

The Greeks and Romans had playwrights such as Aristophanes (450?–380? BCE) and Plautus (254?–184? BCE) who successfully used humor as a type of mirror on the social and political customs of the time. They wrote plays that highlighted some of the particularities of the rich and powerful as well as common people. An early type of comedian was the fool or jester attached to a royal court, whose function it was to entertain by singing, dancing, telling jokes, riddles, and humorous stories, and even by impersonating the king and other members of the aristocracy. In later years, the English playwright William Shakespeare (1564–1616) and the French playwright Moliere (1622–73) used wit and humor to point out some of the shortcomings of society. In the nineteenth century, as cities became more and more crowded, comedy became an especially important diversion for people, and minstrel shows, burlesque, and vaudeville became very popular. These shows usually featured a combination of song, comedy, and other acts, such as magic or acrobatics. Many of the popular comedians of the twentieth century began their careers in burlesque and vaudeville, and hundreds of theaters opened in the United States catering to this form of entertainment. A distinctive part of vaudeville was the great variety of acts presented during a single show. Comedians especially had to work hard to catch the audience's attention and make themselves memorable among all the other performers. Vaudeville provided a training ground for many of the most popular comedians of the twentieth century, including stars such as Bud Abbott and Lou Costello, Milton Berle, Mae West, Bob Hope, the Marx Brothers, George Burns and Gracie Allen, W. C. Fields, and Will Rogers. Vaudeville soon faced competition from the film industry. People flocked to this new form of entertainment, and many of the vaudeville theaters closed or converted to showing moving pictures. For comedians, the new form proved ideal; during the early years of cinema, slapstick films starring the Keystone Cops, Buster Keaton, Charlie Chaplin, Fatty Arbuckle, and many others became immensely popular. Radio also provided a venue for many comedians, and people would gather around a living room radio to hear the performances of stars such as Milton Berle, Edgar Bergen, Jack Benny, and Jimmy Durante. When sound was added to the films in the late 1920s and early 1930s, these comedians were able to adapt their stand-up and radio routines and numbered among the most popular stars in the United States and throughout the world.

Later, television provided another venue for comedians. Milton Berle was one of the very first television stars. The Ed Sullivan show became an important place for comedians to launch their acts to a national audience. Many comedians developed their own television shows, and many more comedians found work writing jokes and scripts for this comedic medium.

Stand-up, that is, live performances before an audience, continued to be one of the most important ways for a comedians to develop an act and perfect the timing, delivery, and other skills a comedian needs. Stand-up comedians did more than simply make people laugh—they attempted to make people think. Current events continued to provide a rich source for material, and the stand-up comedian was often a social critic who used humor as the medium for the message. For example, in the early 1960s Lenny Bruce caused a great deal of controversy in the United States by using his nightclub routines to question the role of organized religion in society and to argue against censorship. During the 1960s, comedians, such as members of the Second City theater group of Chicago, began to adapt improvisational acting techniques, creating a new form of comedic theater. Many of these actor/comedians—from John Belushi to John Candy and many others—went on to stardom.

Stand-up comedy continues to provide an important training ground for comedians. Most of the biggest comedy stars, such as Steve Martin, Jerry Seinfeld, Roseanne, Richard Pryor, Tim Allen, Eddie Murphy, Ellen Degeneres, and many others had their starts as stand-up comedians. During the 1980s, hundred of new comedy clubs opened across the country, providing more venues for comedians to hone their craft than ever before.

Nature of the Work

Although making people laugh may sound like a pretty simple assignment, comedians work very hard at this task. There are many types of comedy, from physical and slapstick comedy to comedy involving highly sophisticated wordplay, but all comedians must work hard to develop their own style. Comedians may use colorful costumes, music, props, or other techniques to create a festive atmosphere, or they may appear in regular attire. In any case, it is the writing and timing that makes a comedian unique. Each comedian attempts to develop a style that presents events in a humorous and memorable way.

Perhaps the most common form of comedic performance is the stand-up comic. Stand-up comedians usually perform in nightclubs or comedy clubs, entertaining audiences with jokes, stories, and impressions. Most often, stand-up comics write their own material, and spend a great deal of time developing, perfecting, and rehearsing new material. Adding new material, and even creating an entirely new routine, is a constant challenge for the comedian.

Stand-up comedians often travel around the country, performing in a variety of settings. They may have to adapt their performances somewhat, depending on the makeup of the audience. The length of the performance is determined by whether the comedian is the main act or an opening act. A main act will last from thirty minutes to an hour, while an opening act may be just a few minutes.

Another popular type of comedy show is the comedy improvisational group. Improvisation is a form of acting in which no set script is used and actors make up their own dialogue as they go along. The improvisational form allows for a kind of spontaneity that traditional performances do not. These groups perform comedic skits and dances, sing humorous songs, and otherwise amuse their audiences. Many comedy groups will perform a number of scripted skits and then improvise a number of skits based on audience suggestions.

Comedians are storytellers. No matter where they perform, they engage their audiences and make the audiences care about their characters. Many comedians use their own life stories as material, weaving a picture of people and places designed not only to evoke laughter but also understanding.

Comedians may perform their work live or on tape. Usually a taping is done in front of an audience, as comedians need the laughter and other feedback of an audience to be most effective.

Comedians who perform on film or television have the same restrictions as other actors and actresses. They must adhere to strict schedules and perform routines repeatedly before the director decides a scene is finished. *Film and television comedians* usually perform scenes that someone else has written, and they are required to memorize their lines and rehearse their performances.

As with other performance artists, comedians often find themselves looking for employment. Comedians may work for a number of weeks in a row and then face a period of unemployment. To find work, many comedians hire booking agents to locate club owners willing to hire them; many clubs feature open mike nights, in which anyone may perform, and these provide important opportunities for beginning comedians. Other comedians attempt to find work on their own. A person's success in finding work will be largely influenced by skill and style, but also to an extent by personal contacts and a bit of good fortune.

For comedians who are uncomfortable in front of an audience, there is the opportunity to write material for other performers. Not all people who write comedic material are former comedians, but all understand elements of humor and ways of using words and images to make people laugh.

Requirements

The overriding requirement for a comedian is to be funny. Comedians should also have a love of performing and a strong desire to make people laugh. There are no set educational standards, and few colleges and universities offer specific courses on how to become a comedian. However, higher education may give a comedian a stronger understanding of society and current events, which may be useful to creating a routine. Nevertheless, becoming a comedian is not a secret. It takes a lot of hard work and, as with other performance skills, practice, practice, practice. Many communities have improvisational groups that provide a training ground for aspiring actors and comedians. Some comedy clubs may also offer classes.

Making people laugh is not a skill that is easily taught. Most good comedians have an inborn talent and have made jokes or performed humorous skits since childhood. This usually means more than simply being the class clown; it is the ability to see events in a humorous light and share this perspective with others. Above all else, a comedian must have a keen sense of timing. A funny line, delivered improperly, often sounds rather ordinary.

Comedians come in all shapes and sizes. Indeed, it is often the person who looks and feels somewhat different who is able to see the foibles of human nature and develop material that pokes fun at society without being nasty. A comedian should be able to take material from his or her own background (be it growing up in a small town, having overbearing parents, or other situations) and interpret this material in a way that appeals to others.

A comedian should obviously have good communications skills and be able to write in a succinct and humorous manner. It is also necessary to have a strong stage presence. Often, budding comedians will take English and composition classes, as well as speech and acting courses, to help develop skills in these areas. Accounting and bookkeeping skills are also helpful, as comedians usually have to prepare their own financial records.

Comedians should be keen observers of daily life and be perceptive enough to recognize the humor in day-to-day events. But comedians should not be overly sensitive and become unduly disappointed if audiences do not respond to their jokes at every performance. It may take years to develop the skills to be a successful comedian, and even the most successful comedians can have an off night.

Opportunities for Experience & Exploration

The field of comedy offers a number of good opportunities for career exploration. For example, many improvisational groups offer classes in acting and performance techniques. These groups are often highly competitive, but they are a good place to learn skills, make contacts, and have fun. Of course, there is no substitute for hands-on experience, and most comedy clubs and coffee houses have open mike nights where all aspiring comedians can get on stage and try out their material in front of a real audience. To get an idea of what it is like to perform before an audience, aspiring comedians can also stage performances for family and friends before venturing on stage to perform for strangers. Acting in school plays and local productions is another good way to get experience. It is also possible to learn by watching. Going to a comedy club or coffee house to observe comedians is a good way to learn about the performance aspects of this career. It is also possible to talk informally with a comedian and in this way learn more about the profession. There are also a number of books that describe exercises and techniques for comedians.

Methods of Entering

Getting started as a comedian is often very difficult. There are thousands of people who want to make people laugh, but relatively few venues for aspiring comedians to get exposure.

To find an opportunity to perform, a comedian may have to repeatedly call local nightclubs, bars, or coffee houses. Generally, these clubs will already have a number of comedians they use.

A common way for a comedian to get his or her first break is to attend open mike nights and call for auditions at a local club. These auditions are not private showings for club owners, but rather actual performances in front of audiences. Usually, comedians are not paid at these auditions, but those who show the most promise are often invited back to put on paid performances.

Many comedians also begin their careers as part of a comedy improvisational group. These groups offer novice comedians a chance to refine their skills, developing techniques and contacts before starting out on their own. Joining many of these groups can be highly competitive; often, an aspiring comedian may join a lesser-known improv group, while working on skills and auditioning for better-known groups.

Another way to break into comedy is through acting. Actors with a flair for comedy can audition for film comedies and situation comedy series. Much of the cast of the hit comedy series *Friends,* for example, came from an acting background.

Advancement

Many comedians begin work as stand-up comedians at local clubs while others begin as part of an improvisation group. Those who find success and satisfaction at this level may go on to perform at larger clubs and theaters. Some may also find work in the corporate world, entertaining at trade shows and other meetings. Extremely successful comedians may go on to tape comedy routines for broadcast or even have their own television shows.

Comedians may also branch out somewhat in their career goals. Some may choose to write material for other comedians or review comedic performances for the local media. There are also some who choose to become comedy club owners or talent agents, creating employment opportunities for other comedians.

Comedy writers may go on to work for advertising agencies, using humor as a means of creating commercials or other promotional materials. Others may develop television or movie scripts.

Employment Outlook

As with the other performance arts, there will always be more people who want to be comedians than there are job opportunities. Comedians, however, enjoy more solid employment prospects than actors or actresses. There are hundreds of comedy clubs across the country (usually in larger cities) and each club needs performers to get their audiences laughing. During the 1990s, the boom in comedy clubs slowed; however, new venues, such as the spread of legalized gambling across the United States, and the opening of many resorts and theme parks, continue to add new opportunities for comedians. Of course, the most lucrative jobs will go to those with the best reputation, but thousands of comedians will continue to find work into the next century.

There is also a growing trend for private companies to hire comedians to perform at sales meetings and trade shows. Comedians help to increase interest in products and create an enjoyable sales environment. Talent agencies now increasingly book comedians to work at these events.

For those who choose to work as comedy writers or entertainment critics, the competition for jobs should be keen, yet there are good career opportunities. The growth of the cable television industry in particular has created a need for increasing numbers of writers to work on the growing number of new shows. There are a large number of comedy shows on the national networks and on cable television, and these should provide a good market for skilled comedy writers.

Earnings

People who only look at the incomes of well-known comedians will get a mistaken notion of how much comedians earn. Jim Carrey may earn millions for a single movie, other comedy stars may earn $200,000 for one performance, but the vast majority of comedians earn far lower wages. In fact, most comedians must hold full- or part-time jobs to supplement the income from their performances.

In large comedy clubs, a headline comedian can expect to earn between $1,000 and $20,000 per show, depending on his or her drawing power. Those who perform as an opening act might earn between $125 and $350 per show. Headline comedians at smaller clubs will earn between $300 and $800 per show. Comedians hired to perform college shows earn around $500 per show. Of course, those just starting out will earn very little (remember, most club owners do not pay comedians who are auditioning), and start at as little as fifteen to twenty dollars for a twenty minute set; yet beginners will be in a good position to learn the craft and make valuable contacts.

Comedians who entertain at trade shows and sales meetings can earn several hundred dollars per show, yet these assignments tend to be infrequent.

Comedy writers have a very wide pay scale. Those who write for well-known comedians are paid about $50 for every joke used. (Of course, many jokes are rejected by the performer.) Full-time comedy writers for the *Tonight Show* and other television shows can expect to earn between $50,000 and $150,000 per year, depending on their skill, experience, and the budget of the show.

Conditions of Work

Full-time comedians usually spend a lot of time traveling between shows. A comedian may have a strong following in the Midwest, for example, and in the course of a week have two shows in Detroit, two shows in Chicago, and a show in St. Louis. Some people may find this lifestyle exciting, but for many it is exhausting and lonely. Those who perform as part of an improv troupe may also travel a lot. Once a comedian has developed a good following, the traveling may subside somewhat. Often, a comedian will perform at one or two clubs in the same city on a fairly regular basis.

Performing in front of an audience can be very demanding. Not all audiences are receptive (especially to new material) and a comedian may encounter unresponsive crowds. It is also not uncommon for comedians to perform for small audiences in bars and nightclubs. Many of these nightclubs may be small, dark, and filled with smoke.

Despite these challenges, comedians can have fascinating careers. They experience the thrill of performing in front of audiences, and having an impact on people's lives. Comedians may go on to achieve a good deal of fame, especially those who perform on television or in the movies. As creative artists, comedians may find it very satisfying to express their views and get positive feedback from others. There can be a lot of pleasure in making people laugh and seeing others enjoy themselves.

Comedians usually work late into the night, often not starting performances until 9 PM or 10 PM. They also generally work weekends, when people have more time to go to nightclubs and comedy clubs. For those who work as part-time comedians, it is not uncommon to have a day job and then perform at night.

Comedy writers may also have to work at other jobs to make ends meet financially. They might prepare material in their homes or in small offices with other writers.

Sources of Additional Information

■ **The Association of Comedy Artists**
PO Box 1796
New York, NY 10025
Tel: 212-864-6620

■ **National Comedians Association**
581 9th Avenue
New York, NY 10036
Tel: 212-875-7705

Composers

School Subjects
Music, Theater/dance

Personal Interests
Entertaining, Music

Work Environment
Primarily indoors, Primarily one location

Minimum Education Level
High school diploma

Salary Range
$1,500 to $150,000

Certification or Licensing
None

Outlook
Little change or more slowly than the average

DOT
152

GOE
01.04.02

NOC
5132

Definition

Composers create much of the music heard every day on radio and television, in theaters and concert halls, on recordings and in advertising, and through any other medium of musical presentation. Composers write symphonies, concertos, and operas; scores for theater, television, and cinema; and music for musical theater, recording artists, and commercial advertising. They may combine elements of classical music with elements of popular musical styles such as rock, jazz, reggae, folk, and others.

History

This article focuses on composers of classical music; composers of popular music are discussed in a separate entry, under "Songwriters." Many composers create music in both popular and classical forms. The term "classical" is rather vague. The Classical Period in music extended from the mid-eighteenth through the nineteenth century. However, the word "classical" is sometimes used to cover all "serious" music, such as symphonies, operas, concerti, and sonatas, among others, and includes contemporary music, much of which has broken in style and form with the classical works.

Classical (used in the widest sense) composition probably dates back to the late Middle Ages, when musical notation began to develop in Christian monasteries. In those times and for some centuries thereafter, the church was the main patron of musical composition. During the fourteenth century, or possibly earlier, the writing of music in score (that is, for several instruments or instruments and voices) began to take place. This was the beginning of orchestral writing. Composers then were mostly sponsored by the church and were supposed to be religiously motivated in their work, which was not to be considered an expression of their own emotions. It was probably not until the end of the fifteenth century that the work of a composer began to be recognized as a statement of individual expression. Recognition of composers did not really become common until several centuries later. Even Johann Sebastian Bach (1685–1750), writing in the eighteenth century, was known more as an organist and choirmaster during his lifetime.

The writing of music in score was the beginning of a great change in the history of music. The craft of making musical instruments and the techniques of playing them were advancing also By the beginning of the Baroque Period, around 1600, these changes brought musical composition to a new stage of development, which was enhanced by patronage from secular sources. The nobility had taken an interest in sponsoring musical composition, and over the next two to three hundred years they came to supplant the church as the main patrons of composers. Under their patronage, composers had more room to experiment and develop new musical styles.

During the Baroque Period, which lasted until about 1750, there was a flowering of musical forms, including opera. In the early 1600s, Rome became preeminent in opera, using the chorus and dance to embellish the operatic spectacle. Instrumental music also grew during the Baroque Period, reaching its greatest flowering in the work of Johann Sebastian Bach and George Frederick Handel (1685–1759). The major musical forms of Baroque origin were the sonata and cantata, both largely attributed to the composers of opera.

The "true" Classical Period in music began in about the mid-eighteenth century and lasted through the nineteenth century. Composers embellishing the sonata form now developed the symphony. Through the latter half of the nineteenth century, most composers of symphonies, concerti, chamber music, and other instrumental forms adhered to the strict formality of the Classical tradition. In the nineteenth century, however, many composers broke from Classical formalism, instilling greater emotionalism, subjectivity, and individualism in their work. The new musical style evolved into what became formally known as the Romantic movement in music. Romanticism did not replace classicism, but rather, existed side by side with the older form. A transitional figure in the break from classicism was Ludwig van Beethoven (1770–1827), whose compositions elevated the symphonic form to its highest level. Other composers who perfected the Romantic style included Franz Schubert (1797--1828), Franz Liszt (1811–86), Johannes Brahms (1833–97), Hector Berlioz (1803–69), and Peter Ilich Tchaikovsky (1840–93) in orchestral music, and Giuseppe Verdi (1813–1901) and Richard Wagner (1813–83) in opera.

Many of the composers of the early Classical period labored for little more than recognition. Their monetary rewards were often meager. In the nineteenth century, however, as the stature of the composers grew, they were able to gain more control over their own work and the proceeds that it produced. The opera composers, in particular, were able to reap quite handsome profits.

Another abrupt break from tradition occurred at the beginning of the twentieth century. At that time composers began to turn away from Romanticism and seek new and original styles and sounds. Audiences sometimes were repulsed by these new musical sounds, but eventually they were accepted and imitated by other composers. One of the most successful of the post-Romantic composers was Igor Stravinsky (1882–1971), whose landmark work *The Rite of Spring* was hailed by some to be the greatest work of the century.

Through the twentieth century composers continued to write music in the styles of the past and to experiment with new styles. Some contemporary composers, such as George Gershwin (1898–1937) and Leonard Bernstein (1918–90), wrote for both the popular and serious audiences. John Cage (1912–95), Philip Glass, Steve Reich, and other composers moved even further from traditional forms and musical instruments, experimenting with electronically created music, in which an electronic instrument, such as a synthesizer, is used to compose and play music. An even more significant advance is the use of computers as a compositional tool. As the twenty-first century approaches, the only thing predictable in musical composition is that experimentation and change are certain to continue.

Nature of the Work

A composer expresses himself in music much as a writer expresses himself with words and a painter with line, shape, and color. Composing is hard work. Although he has been influenced by what he has heard, the composer's compositions are original because they reflect his own interpretation and use of musical elements. All composers use the same basic musical elements, including harmony, melody, counterpoint, and rhythm, but each composer applies these elements in his own unique way. Music schools teach all of the elements that go into composition, providing the composer with the tools that he needs for his work—but how he uses these tools to create music is what sets him apart.

There is no prescribed way for a composer to go about composing. All composers work in a somewhat different way, but generally speaking they pursue their work in some kind of regular, patterned way, in much the same fashion of a novelist or a painter. Composers may work in different areas of classical music, writing, for example, symphonies, operas, concerti, music for a specific instrument or grouping of instruments, and for voice. Many composers also work in popular music, and incorporate popular music ideas in their classical compositions.

A composer may create a composition out of sheer inspiration, with or without a particular market in mind, or she may be commissioned to write a piece of music for a particular purpose. Composers who write music on their own then have the problem of finding someone to perform their music in the hopes that it will be well received and lead to further performances and possibly a recording. The more a composer's music is played and recorded, the greater the chances to sell future offerings and to receive commissions for new work. Commissions come from institutions (where the composer may or may not be a faculty member), from societies and associations, and orchestral groups, or from film, television, and commercial projects. Almost every film has a score—the music playing throughout the film apart from any songs that may also be in the film.

A composer who wishes to make his living by writing music should understand the musical marketplace as well as possible. It should be understood that only a small percentage of music composers can make their living solely by writing music. To make a dent in the marketplace one should be familiar with its major components:

Performance. Composers usually rely on one of two ways to have their music performed: they contact musical performers or producers who are most likely to be receptive to their style of composition, or they may write for a musical group in which they are performers.

Music Publishing. Music publishers seek composers who are talented and whose work they feel it will be profitable to promote. They take a cut of the royalties, but they relieve composers of all of the business and legal detail of their profession. Composers today have rather commonly turned to self-publishing.

Copying. A musical composition written for several pieces or voices requires copying into various parts. Composers may do this work themselves, but it is an exacting task for which professional copiers may be employed. Many composers themselves take on copying work as a sideline.

Computerization. Computers have become an increasingly important tool for composing and copying. Some composers have set up incredibly sophisticated computerized studios in which they compose, score, and play an orchestrated piece by computer. They can also do the copying and produce a recording. Perhaps the most significant enhancement to the home studio is the Musical Instrument Digital Interface (MIDI), which transposes the composer's work into computer language and then converts it into notation.

Recording. Knowing the recording industry is an important aspect in advancing a composer's career. An unrecognized composer will find it difficult to catch on with a commercial recording company, but it is not uncommon for a composer to make his own recording and handle the distribution and promotion as well.

Film and Television. There is a very large market for original compositions in feature and industrial films, television programs, and videos. The industry is in constant need of original scores and thematic music.

Students interested in composing can tap into any number of organizations and associations for more detail on any area of musical composition. One such organization providing support and information is Meet the Composer, which is headquartered in New York City and has several national affiliates.

Requirements

There is no specific course of training that leads one to become a composer. Many composers begin composing from a very early age, and receive tutoring and training to encourage their talent. Musically inclined students should continue their private studies and take advantage of everything musical their high school offers. Specially gifted students usually find their way to schools or academies that specialize in music or the arts. These students may begin learning composition in this special environment, and some might begin to create original compositions.

After high school the musical student can continue his education in any of numerous colleges and universities or special music schools or conservatories that offer bachelor's and higher degrees. The composer's course of study includes courses on music history, music criticism, music theory, harmony, counterpoint, rhythm, melody, and ear training. In most major music schools courses in composition are offered along with orchestration and arranging. Courses are also taught covering voice and the major musical instruments, including keyboard, guitar, and, more recently, synthesizer. Most schools now cover computer techniques as applied to music, as well. It may also be helpful to learn at least one foreign language; German, French, and Italian are good choices. Prospective composers are advised to become proficient on at least one instrument.

None of this is to say that study in a musical institution is required for a composer, or is any guarantee of success. Some say that composing cannot be taught, that the combination of skills, talent, and inspiration required to create music is a highly individual occurrence. Authorities have argued on both sides of this issue without resolution. It does appear that genetics plays a strong part in musical ability; musical people often come from musical families. There are many contradictions of this, however, and some authorities site the musical environment as being highly influential. The great composers were extraordinarily gifted, and it is very possible that even achieving moderate success in music requires special talent. Nevertheless, there will be little success without hard work and dedication.

Opportunities for Experience & Exploration

Musical programs offered by local schools, YMCAs, and community centers offer good beginning opportunities. It is especially helpful to learn to play a musical instrument, such as the piano, violin, or cello. Attending concerts and recitals and reading about music and musicians and their careers will also provide good background and experience. There are also any number of videos available through schools and libraries that teach young people about music. Young musicians should form or join musical groups and attempt to write music for the groups to perform. There are also many books that provide good reference information on careers in composing.

Methods of Entering

In school, young composers should try to have their work performed either at school concerts or by local school or community ensembles. This will also most likely involve the composer in copying and scoring his work, and possibly even directing. Student film projects can provide an opportunity for experience at film composing and scoring. Working in school or local musical theater companies can provide valuable experience. Personal connections made in these projects may be very helpful in the professional world that lies ahead. Developing a portfolio of work will be helpful as the composer enters a professional career.

Producers of public service commercials for radio, television, and film are frequently on the lookout for *pro bono* (volunteer) work that can provide opportunities for young, willing composers. Such opportunities may be listed in trade magazines, such as *Variety* and *Show Business.*

Joining the American Federation of Musicians and other musical societies and associations is another good move for aspiring composers. Among the associations that can be contacted are Meet the Composer, the American Composers Alliance, and ASCAP, all in New York City. These associations and the trade papers are also good sources for leads on grants and awards for which composers can apply.

Young composers, songwriters, and jingle writers can also work their way into the commercial advertising business, by doing some research and taking an entry-level job with an agency that handles musical commercials.

Advancement

Moving ahead in the music world is strictly done on an individual basis. There is no hierarchical structure to climb, although in record companies a person with music writing talent might move into a producing or A&R job and be able to exercise compositional skills in those capacities. There might be a few "house" composer jobs in advertising agencies or studios that make commercials, or at film, television, and video production studios. Schools often underwrite a composer in residence, and many composers work as professors in college and university music departments while continuing to compose. For the most part, however, the composer is on his own to create and promote his work. Advancement is based on talent, determination, and, probably, luck. Some composers become well known for their work with film scores—John Williams, of *Star Wars* fame is one.

Advancement for a composer often takes place on a highly personal level. They may progress through their careers to writing music of greater complexity and in more challenging structures. They may develop a unique style, and even develop new forms and traditions of music. One day, their name might be added to the list of the great composers.

Employment Outlook

The employment outlook for composers probably does not change from year to year in the United States and is one field that does not respond to economic cycles of recession and prosperity. There are no reliable statistics on the number of people who make their living solely from composing, except that the general consensus is that very few people can sustain themselves through composing alone. The field is highly competitive and is crowded with highly talented people trying to have their music published and played. There are only a limited number of commissions, grants, and awards available at any time, and the availability of these is often subjected to changes in the economy. On the other hand, many films continue to be made each year, particularly as cable television companies produce more and more original programs. However, the chances of new composers supporting themselves by their music alone will likely always remain rare.

Earnings

A few composers make huge annual incomes while many make little or nothing. Some make a very large income in one or two years and none in succeeding years. While many composers receive royalties on repeat performances of their work, most depend on commissions to support themselves. Commissions vary widely according to the type of work, and the industry for which the work will be performed. A survey conducted by Meet the Composer in 1992 offers a breakdown of typical commissions.

In concert music and jazz compositions, commissions range according to the length of the work and the number of musicians who will play the work. A piece for solo or duo instruments of ten minutes in length may be commissioned for $1,500 to $4,000; a ten to twenty-five-minute piece receives between $2,500 to $10,000; and a piece over twenty-five minutes can receive $7,500 to $15,000 or more. Commissions increase with the complexity of performance, through piano solo or duo with instrument or voice, trio or quartet, chorus, small or large chamber orchestra, and full orchestra concerto.

Composers for dance works and companies generally receive a similar range of commission fees.

Incidental music composed for the theater receives commissions based on the size and type of the theater company or play. A regional company may pay in the $3,000 to $8,000 range, an off-Broadway show pays from $3,000 to $6,000, and a Broadway show pays $5,000 to $12,000. In musical theater, advances up to $10,000 against royalties may be received by the composer. Each composer negotiates his or her own royalty rate, generally a percentage of the box office receipts.

Opera companies commission works for one-act operas and full-length operas. A small company may pay in the range of $10,000 to $20,000 for a one-act opera and $30,000 to $70,000 for a full-length opera. Large opera companies pay from $15,000 to $40,000 for a one-act opera, and from $75,000 to $150,000 for a full-length opera.

The music budget for a film ranges from 1 percent to 10 percent of the total production. A film for a major studio may pay a composer $50,000 to $200,000 or more for a musical score. An independent or television film may pay in the range of $5,000 to $100,000. Documentary films pay in the range of $2,000 to $20,000.

For a television program or series, a composer may be paid per episode, ranging from $1,000 to $8,000, depending on the length of the episode, and whether for a network, cable, or independent television company. Composers for advertising generally receive a flat fee of 10 to 20 percent of a commercial's budget. Payment ranges from $300 for a regional commercial, up to $20,000 or more for a national commercial, and up to $50,000 if the music is to be a musical "logo"—one that identifies the company or product advertised.

Conditions of Work

The physical conditions of a composer's workplace can vary according to personal taste and what is affordable. Some work in expensive, state-of-the-art home studios, others in a bare room with an electric keyboard or a guitar. An aspiring art composer may work in a cramped and cluttered room in a New York City tenement, or a Hollywood ranch home.

For the serious art composer the work is likely to be personally rewarding, but financially unrewarding. For the commercial writer, some degree of financial reward is more likely, but competition is fierce, and the big prize goes only to the rarest of individuals. Getting started requires great dedication and sacrifice. Even those protected by academia must give up most of their spare time to composing, often sitting down to the piano when exhausted from a full day of teaching. There are many frustrations along the way. The career composer must learn to live with rejection and have the verve and determination to keep coming back time and again. Under these circumstances, a composer can only succeed by having complete faith in his own work.

Sources of Additional Information

■ **American Composers Alliance**
170 West 74th Street
New York, NY 10023
Tel: 212-362-8900

■ **American Federation of Musicians of the United States and Canada**
1501 Broadway, Suite 600
New York, NY 10036
Tel: 212-869-1330

■ **American Society of Composers, Authors, and Publishers (ASCAP)**
One Lincoln Plaza
New York, NY 10023
Tel: 212-595-3050

■ **American Women Composers, Inc.**
c/o George Washington University
Department of Music
B-144 The Academic Center
Washington, DC 20052
Tel: 202-994-6338

For information regarding grant programs and general career information, contact:

■ **Meet the Composer, Inc.**
2112 Broadway, Suite 505
New York, NY 10023
Tel: 212-787-3601

■ **National Association of Composers, USA (NACUSA)**
PO Box 49652, Barrington Station
Los Angeles, CA 90049
Tel: 310-541-8213

■ **Society of Composers**
PO Box 296
Old Chelsea Station
New York, NY 10013-0296
Tel: 718-899-2605

Costume Designers

School Subjects
Home economics, Theater/dance

Personal Interests
Clothes, Drawing/painting

Work Environment
Primarily indoors, One location with some travel

Minimum Education Level
High school diploma

Salary Range
$400 to $17,500+ per production

Certification or Licensing
None

Outlook
About as fast as the average

DOT
142

GOE
01.02.03

NOC
5243

Definition

Costume designers plan and create clothing and accessories for all characters in a stage, film, television, dance, or opera production.

History

Costume design has been an important part of the theater since the early Greek tragedies, when actors wore masks and long robes with sleeves, unlike the dress of the day. By the time of the Roman Caesars, stage costumes had become very elaborate and colorful.

After the fall of Rome, theater disappeared for some time, but it returned in the form of Easter and Nativity plays. Priests and choirboys wore their usual robes with some simple additions, such as veils and crowns. Plays then moved from the church to the marketplace, and costumes again became important.

During the Renaissance, fantastic mythological costumes were designed for the Italian intermezzi, triumphs, and pageants, the French *ballets de coeur*, and the English masques by such famous designers as Torelli, Jean Berain, and Burnacini. From 1760 to 1782, Louis-Rene Boquet designed costumes using wide paniers, forming a kind of ballet skirt covered with rococo detail. But by the end of the eighteenth century, there was a movement toward more classical costumes on the stage.

During the early nineteenth century, historical costumes became popular, and Elizabethan, Stuart, and other details were added to contemporary dress. Toward the end of the nineteenth century, realism became important, and actors wore the dress of the day, often their own clothes. Since this trend meant fewer jobs for costume designers, they turned to lighter musical productions and opera to express their creativity.

In the early twentieth century, Diaghilev's Russian Ballet introduced a non-naturalism in costumes, most notably in the designs of Leon Bakst. This trend gave way to European avant-garde theater, in which costumes became abstract and symbolic.

Since the 1960s, new materials, such as plastics and adhesives, have greatly increased the costume designer's range. Costume design is less likely to conform to trends.

Nature of the Work

Costume designers generally work as freelancers. After they have been contracted to provide the costumes for a production, they first read the script to find out the theme, geographical location, time period, who the characters are, their relationships and functions, the kind of dialogue, and action. They meet with the director to learn his or her interpretation, discussing characters, period and style, the time frame for the production, and the budget.

For a play, designers then plan a rough costume plot, which is a list of costume changes by scene for each character. They research the history thoroughly. They plan a preliminary color scheme and sketch the costumes, including gloves, footwear, hose, purses, jewelry, umbrellas, canes, fans, bouquets, and masks. The costume designer or an assistant collects swatches of fabrics and samples of various accessories.

After completing the research, final color sketches are painted or drawn and mounted for presentation. Once the director approves the designs, the costume designer solicits bids from contractors; finds, pulls, or rents costumes; and shops for fabrics, notions, trim, and accessories. Measurements of all actors are taken. Designers work closely with drapers and sewers in costume shops, hairstylists, and makeup artists. They supervise fittings and attend all dress rehearsals to make final adjustments and repairs.

Costume designers work in films, television programs, and videos, providing a look that will highlight the character's personality. They may design and create costumes for individual performers, such as figure skaters, ballroom dance competitors, clowns, circus performers, theme park characters, as well as rock groups and artists, and any other performers who routinely wear costumes as part of their performance.

Requirements

Costume designers need at least a high school education. A college degree is not a requirement, but in this highly competitive field, it gives a sizable advantage, and most costume designers today have a bachelor's degree. Many art schools, especially in New York and Los Angeles, have BFA and MFA programs in costume design. A liberal arts school that has a strong theater program is also a good choice.

Costume designers need sewing, draping, and flat patterning skills, as well as training in basic design techniques and figure drawing. English, literature, and history classes help students learn how to analyze a play and research the clothing and manner of various historical periods. Marketing and business-related classes will be helpful, as most costume designers work as freelancers. Costume designers must prepare a portfolio of their work, including three or four dozen photographs and sketches from two or three shows.

Some theatrical organizations require membership in United Scenic Artists, a union that protects the interests of designers on the job and sets minimum fees. Beginning designers become members by passing an exam. More experienced designers must submit a portfolio for review.

Opportunities for Experience & Exploration

Those interested in a costume design career should join a theater organization, such as a school drama club or a community theater. School dance troupes or film classes also may offer opportunities to explore costume design.

The *Costumer's Handbook* and *The Costume Designer's Handbook*, both by Rosemary Ingham and Elizabeth Covey, are invaluable resources for beginning or experienced costume designers. Both books explain in detail the various steps in the costume design process. Prospective costume designers can practice designing on their own, drawing sketches in a sketchbook, and copying designs they see on television, in films, or on the stage. They can also practice making costumes for themselves, friends and family, and dolls.

Methods of Entering

Most high schools and colleges have drama clubs and dance groups that need costumes designed and made. Community theaters, too, may offer opportunities for design students to assist in costume production. Regional theaters hire several hundred costume technicians each year for seasons that vary from twenty-eight to fifty weeks.

Many beginning designers enter the field by becoming an assistant to a successful designer. Established designers welcome newcomers and are generous mentors.

Some start working at costume shops, which require membership in the International Ladies Garment Workers Union, but they may hire nonunion workers for specific time periods. Some begin as shoppers, who swatch fabrics, compare prices, and buy yardage, trim, and accessories. This is a great way to learn where to find materials and how much they cost and also helps a prospective designer make valuable contacts in the field. Other positions good for beginners are: *milliner's assistant, craft assistant,* or *assistant to the draper.*

Schools with BFA or MFA programs in costume design may offer internships that can lead to jobs after graduation. Another method of entering costume design, though less successful, is to write to regional theaters and send your resume to the theater's managing director.

Before you become a costume designer, you may find it advisable to work as a freelance design assistant for a few years until you have acquired experience, reputation, contacts, and an impressive portfolio.

Advancement

Beginning designers must show they are willing to do a variety of tasks. The theater community is small and intricately interconnected, so if you work hard and are flexible, you will gain a good reputation quickly. Smaller regional theaters tend to hire designers for a full season to work with the same people on one or more productions, so the opportunities for movement are few.

Eventually, costume designers with experience and talent can work for films, television, and videos.

Employment Outlook

Theater budgets and support for the arts in general have come under pressure in recent years and have limited employment prospects for costume designers. Many theaters, especially small and nonprofit theaters, are cutting their budgets or doing smaller shows that require few costumes. The cable television business, however, is growing rapidly and will continue to grow in the next decade. As more cable television networks create original programming, demand for costume design in this area is likely to increase.

New York City is the main proving ground for theater designers, as Hollywood is for film designers. Costume design, however, is becoming more decentralized because of the number of regional theaters throughout the United States and because cable television companies operate at locations across the country. As a result, designers must be willing to travel.

Competition is stiff and will remain so throughout the next decade, depending on the economy. The number of qualified costume designers far exceeds the number of jobs available. This is especially true in smaller cities and regions, where there are fewer theaters.

Earnings

Costume designers who work on Broadway or for dance companies in New York City must be members of United Scenic Artists union, which sets minimum fees, requires producers to pay into pension and welfare funds, protects the designer's rights, establishes rules for billing, and offers group health and life insurance.

An assistant on a Broadway show earns about $775. A costume designer for a Broadway musical with a minimum of thirty-six actors earns around $17,500. For opera and dance companies, salary is usually by costume count.

For feature films and television, costume designers earn daily rates for an eight-hour day or a weekly rate for an unlimited number of hours. Designers sometimes earn royalties on their designs.

Regional theaters usually set individual standard fees, which vary widely, beginning around $200 per week for an assistant. Most of them do not require membership in the union.

Most costume designers work freelance and are paid per costume or show. Costume designers can charge $90 to $500 per costume, but some costumes, such as those for figure skaters, can cost thousands of dollars. Freelance costume designers often receive a flat rate for designing costumes for a show. For small and regional theaters, this rate may be in the $400 to $500 range; the flat rate for medium and large productions generally starts at around $1,000. Many costume designers must take second part-time or full-time jobs to supplement their income from costume design.

Freelancers are responsible for their own health insurance, life insurance, and pension plans. They do not receive holiday, sick, or vacation pay.

Conditions of Work

Costume designers put in long hours at painstaking detail work. It is a demanding profession that requires you to be brave, tough, flexible, artistic, and practical. The work can be erratic—a busy period followed by weeks with no work. In spite of the importance of costumes to a production's success, the designer usually gets little recognition compared to the actors and director.

Designers meet a variety of interesting and gifted people. Every play, film, or concert is different and every production situation is unique, so for costume designers there is no steady routine. Costume designers must play many roles: artist, sewer, researcher, buyer, manager, and negotiator.

Sources of Additional Information

■ **Costume Designers Guild**
13949 Ventura Boulevard, Suite 309
Sherman Oaks, CA 91423
Tel: 818-905-1557

■ **The Costume Society of America**
55 Edgewater Drive
PO Box 73
Earleville, MD 21919-0073
Tel: 800-CSA-9447

■ **United Scenic Artists**
16 West 61st Street, 11th Floor
New York, NY 10036
Tel: 212-391-1070

■ **United States Institute of Theater Technology**
10 West 19th Street, Suite 5A
New York, NY 10011
Tel: 212-924-9088
WWW: http://www.ssa.ucalgary.ca/usitt/

Dancers and Choreographers

School Subjects
Music, Theater/dance

Personal Interests
Dancing, Music

Work Environment
Primarily multiple locations, Primarily indoors

Minimum Education Level
High school diploma

Salary Range
$9,600 to $1,100,000

Certification or Licensing
None

Outlook
Faster than the average

DOT
151

GOE
01.05.02

NOC
5134

Definition

Dancers perform dances alone or with others. Through dancing, they attempt to tell a story, interpret an idea, or simply express rhythm and sound by supplying preconceived physical movements to music. *Choreographers* create or develop dance patterns and teach them to performers.

History

Dancing is one of the oldest of the arts. The first formal dances were the ritualistic, symbolic dances of early tribal societies: the dance designed to excite the emotions, such as the war dance; the dance purporting to communicate with the gods, such as the rain dance. Dances are an important part of any culture. In the

United States, for example, the square dance became a part of our folkways. Dancing has become a popular leisure-time activity, a popular form of entertainment, and, for those who provide the entertainment, a career. There are many types of dancing, from ballet to tap dancing, jazz and modern dance, and ballroom dancing.

Ballet has its origins in Italy and France in the fifteenth centuries, when dance was used to help orchestrate a story around a celebration. The early Italian *balletto* combined dance, poetry, song, and elaborate scenery, and a performance could last for hours or days. The balletto was brought to France by Catherine de Medici (1519–89), married to the French king Henry II in 1533, where it was renamed ballet. In the next century King Louis VIX founded L'Academie Royale de Danse, where, under dancing master Pierre Beauchamps, the classical ballet positions were first codified. By the end of the seventeenth century, the French terms had become the international language of ballet. It was not until the beginning of the eighteenth century, however, that ballet became a profession, with its own schools, theaters, paid dancers, and choreographers. As ballet grew, choreographers and dancers developed new ideas, movements, and ideas, and composers began creating music especially for ballet. Noted choreographers and dancers were Jean Philippe Rameau, Franz Hiverding, Jean Georges Noverre, and August Vetris. In the late eighteenth and early nineteenth centuries, choreographers were creating ballets that are still performed today. One of the oldest of such ballets is the French *La Fille Mal Gardee* choreographed by Jean Dauberval. Pointe shoes, and the style of dancing on the toes, were developed toward the middle of the nineteenth century. The end of the nineteenth century saw the creation of many famous ballets, still among the most popular in the world today, including *The Nutcracker Suite, Sleeping Beauty*, and *Swan Lake*. Modern masters of the ballet include Vaslav Nijinsky (1890–1950), Anna Pavlova (1885–1931), George Balanchine (1904–83), Mikhail Fokine (1880–1942), Serge Diaghilev (1872–1929), Margot Fonteyn (born 1919), and more recently, Mikhail Baryshnikov (born 1947), Twyla Tharp (born 1941), and Rudolf Nureyev (1938–1993). In the United States, the Joffrey Ballet and the American Ballet Theatre play important roles in the ballet world.

Modern dance is a distinct art form of the twentieth century. Unlike ballet, modern dance has no set forms or techniques, and is oriented more toward individual expression in its choreography. Rather than presenting an interpretation of a story or narrative, modern dance expresses such abstract concepts as time, space, emotion, or pure movement. The pioneer of modern dance was Isadora Duncan (1878–1927), who introduced the form around the turn of the century. Duncan's lead was followed in 1915 by the creation of the Denishawn School in Los Angeles, considered to be the founder of the modern dance movement. Several dancers from this school went on to form their own schools, including Doris Humphrey (1895–1958) and Charles Weidman (1901–1975), and Martha Graham (1894–1994). In the 1930s, Lester Horton and Helen Tamiris gave rise to another current of modern dance, which went on to inspire the works of Merce Cunningham (born 1922), Alvin Ailey (1931–89), Twyla Tharp, and others.

Tap dancing originated from early Irish and English folk dances, as well as in the African dances brought to the United States by the African slaves. Wearing shoes with metal strips fitted to the heels and toes, tap dance create often complex rhythms by striking their heels and toes on the floor. Developed through minstrel shows, and later through vaudeville, musicals, and film, tap dancing soon became a popular form of entertainment. The first choreographed tap dancing routines were performed by the Floradora Sextet in 1900. Later popularizers of tap dancing included Bill "Bojangles" Robinson (1878–1949), Fred Astaire (1899–1987), and Ruby Keeler (1909-1993), and, in more recent years, Gregory Hines (born1946).

In addition to many traditional folk and ethnic dances, many other dances have developed through the years, including popular ballroom dances such as swing, the fox trot, the tango, the mambo, the cha cha, and others, and more recently popular dances such as salsa, the merengue, and hip-hop.

Nature of the Work

Dancers usually dance together as a chorus. As they advance in their profession, dancers may do special numbers with other selected dancers and, when a reputation is attained, the dancer may do solo work. There are four basic types of dancing, and although some dancers become proficient in all four, most dancers attempt to specialize in one specific area.

The *acrobatic dancer* performs a style of dancing characterized by difficult gymnastic feats.

The *ballet dancer* performs artistic dances suggesting a theme or story. Ballet is perhaps one of the most exacting and demanding forms of dance. Most other types of dancers need some type of ballet training.

The *interpretive* or *modern dancer* (sometimes referred to as a *classical dancer*) performs dances that interpret moods or characterizations. Facial expression and the body are used to express the theme of the dance.

The *tap dancer* performs a style of dancing that is distinguished by rhythm tapped by the feet in time with the music.

In all dancing, grace and execution are basic. Some dances require specific traditional movements and precise positions. Others provide for planned movement but permit sufficient variation in execution.

The dancer thus is able to include a spin, a dip, a pause, or some other effect that provides a certain amount of individuality and flair to the performance.

Dancing is a profession that permits the performers to make the most of their physical features and personality. Part of the success of dancers depends on the ability to use their assets in ways that will permit their full expression.

Dancers may perform in classical ballet or modern dance, in dance adaptations for musical shows, in folk dances, or in tap and other types of popular dancing productions. Some dancers compete in contests for specific types of dancing such as ballroom dancing.

A few dancers have become choreographers, who create new ballets or dance routines. They must be knowledgeable about dancing, music, costume, lighting, and dramatics. Others are dance directors and train the dancers in productions. Many dancers combine teaching with their stage work or are full-time *dance instructors* in ballet schools or in colleges and universities. Some open their own dancing schools with specialties such as ballet for children or ballroom dancing.

A small number of dancers and choreographers work in music videos. While they may not become rich or famous in this line of work, it does provide good experience and increases their visibility.

Requirements

There are no formal educational requirements, but an early start (around eight for ballet) and years of practice are basic to a successful career. The preparation for a professional dancing career is as much a test of one's personal characteristics as it is of one's talent. The aspirant needs, first and foremost, to be enthusiastic about dancing, for the basic desire to achieve success is an ingredient that will help to overcome some of the disappointment and despair that seem to be hurdles normally encountered.

The physical demands of daily practice as well as the demands of the dance routine necessitate good health and a strong body. A dancer must also have a feeling for music, a sense of rhythm, and grace and agility. Good feet with normal arches are required. Persistence and sensitivity, as they apply to the day-to-day preparation of the dancer, are also important personal characteristics.

A good high school education is highly recommended for those interested in becoming dancers. Students should elect courses in speech, music, and dramatics, and engage in extracurricular activities that will enhance their knowledge of these areas. High school students may also continue their dance studies during the summer. Some summer camps feature dance training, and special summer classes are available in some large cities.

A number of avenues for advanced training are available. About 240 colleges and universities offer programs leading to a bachelor's or higher degree in dance, generally through the departments of physical education, music, theater, or fine arts. These programs provide an opportunity for a college education and advanced preparation and training. Other possibilities include study with professional dancing teachers or attendance at a professional dance school. There are a number of such schools in the country; most of them are located in large cities.

Experience as a performer is usually required for teaching in professional schools, and graduate degrees are generally required by colleges and conservatories.

Opportunities for Experience & Exploration

Dancing is a highly competitive profession, and interested students should take advantage of every opportunity to gain experience. It is not too difficult to find places to perform in one's own community, and it is wise to dance publicly early and often. Most dancers continue with classes in dance throughout their professional careers.

Methods of Entering

The only way to get started in dancing is to dance, to take advantage of every performance opportunity possible. Local groups are usually in the market for entertainment at their meetings or social affairs. These appearances provide the opportunity to polish routines and develop the professional air that distinguishes the professional from the amateur performer. Breaking the professional barrier by achieving one's first paid performance can be accomplished in several ways. Take advantage of every audition. Follow the announcements in the trade magazines. Circulate among other dancers. Attend shows and get to know everyone who may be in a position to help with a job. Another possibility that should be considered is to register with recognized booking agents.

Advancement

As in all performing arts, the star on the dressing room door is the dream of dancing aspirants. Yet top billing, a name in lights, or being the program headliner are positions of accomplishment reserved for a very small number. Many dancers start by earning a spot in the dancing chorus of an off-Broadway musical, in the line at a supper club, or in a dancing group on a television variety show or spectacular. Such opportunities permit further study and lessons, yet enable one to work with experienced choreographers and producers. Earning a spot as a chorus dancer in television on a regular weekly show could provide as many as thirteen, twenty-six, or thirty-nine performances with the same group.

In recent years, a number of musical stock companies have originated throughout the United States, thus providing another avenue for employment. Although many of these operate only in summer, they provide experience of a Broadway nature. Outdoor spectaculars such as exhibitions, parades, fairs, and festivals often use dance acts.

Working on the road can be an exciting, yet tiring, opportunity. Chorus groups with traveling musicals and cafe shows provide regular employment for a season. The numbers are rehearsed before the tour and very little adaptation or change is possible. One does get a chance to perform in a variety of situations and with different bands or orchestras because accompaniments are different in each club or community performance.

Dancers may also advance to choreographing, one of the most creative and responsible jobs in dancing. Other dancers find positions as teachers and some eventually open their own schools.

Dancers join various unions depending on the type of dance they perform. The American Guild of Musical Artists is the union to which dancers belong who perform in opera ballets, classical ballet, and modern dance. Those on live or taped television join the American Federation of Television and Radio Artists. Dancers in films have the Screen Actors Guild or the Screen Extras Guild. Those who appear on stage in musical comedies join the Actors' Equity Association. And those who dance in nightclubs and variety shows belong to the American Guild of Variety Artists.

Employment Outlook

Employment of dancers is expected to increase faster than the national occupational average through the next decade, but those seeking a career in dancing will find the field highly competitive and uncertain. For performers, there are limited opportunities since there are more trained dancers than job openings. Television has provided additional positions, but the number of stage and screen productions is declining. The best opportunities may exist in regional ballet companies, opera companies, and dance groups affiliated with colleges and universities. The turnover rate in dancing is rather high so there are always openings for the newcomer. Although generalization is difficult, the average chorus dancer can expect a career of five to ten years at best. Most ballet dancers stop dancing for an audience before they are forty years of age.

The dancer who can move from performing to teaching will find other employment possibilities in colleges, universities, and schools of dance; with civic and community groups; and in the operation of dance studios.

Dancing as a performing career is characterized by irregular employment. There is often a long span of time between engagements. For that reason, it is difficult to calculate the exact number of people employed in this field. In the 1990s, it is estimated that professional dancers hold about 8,600 stage, screen, and TV jobs at any one time. About 3,300 dancers were employed in the 300 U.S. and Canadian modern dance companies; about 5,000 dancers were employed by the 275 ballet companies.

Dancers may find work throughout the United States, but most of the major dance companies are located in New York. Other cities that have full-time dance companies include San Francisco, Chicago, Boston, Philadelphia, Pittsburgh, Miami, and Washington, DC.

Earnings

For the performing dancer, the conditions of employment, the hours of work, and salaries are established in agreements between the unions and the producers. Union contracts set only minimums, however, and a dancer's contract with the employer may contain more favorable terms.

The minimum salary for dancers in ballet and other stage productions is about $610 a week in the 1990s, and can range to $1,275 per week or more for a principal dancer. However, dance contracts rarely cover an entire year; most dance contracts are in the thirty-six- to forty-five-week range. Modern dance companies generally pay a base salary of $500 per week, up to $1,200 per week for a forty-two- to forty-four-week year. Smaller companies, however, pay lower salaries, of around $50 per performance, and $5 per hour of rehearsal time. The single performance rate for new first-year ballet dancers is $230. Dancers on tour are paid extra to cover room and board expenses. Minimum performance rates for dancers on television average $569 for a one-hour show, which generally includes an additional eighteen hours of rehearsal time. Dancers receive extra pay for any additional hours worked, including fees for rehearsal hours.

Payment for dancers in other areas vary. Dancers on cruise ships generally earn between $200 and $500 per week, but receive room and board during a cruise. Dancers for opera and stage performances average about $75 per performance, with an additional $50-$60 per day while touring. Dancers on Broadway earn a minimum of $700 per week.

Many performing dancers must supplement their income with other work. Union contracts provide for various health and welfare benefits. Other dancers must supply their own health insurance, pension plans, and the like.

Earnings for choreographers vary immensely. Earnings from performance royalties and fees range from nearly $1,000 a week in small professional theatres, to over $30,000 for a Broadway production that requires eight to ten weeks of rehearsal time. For big-budget motion pictures, choreographers can earn an average of $3,000 a week, while those who work in television can earn up to $10,000 for a fourteen-day work period.

Conditions of Work

The irregularity of employment is the most difficult aspect of the profession. Dancers are never certain where they will be employed or under what conditions. One may wait weeks for a contract. An offer may involve travel, night hours, or weekend rehearsals. Work on a Broadway stage show may last twenty weeks, forty weeks, or three years, or possibly the show will fold after the third performance. With rehearsals and performances, a normal work week runs thirty hours (six hours a day maximum).

Dancing requires considerable sacrifices of both a personal and social nature. Dancing is the performing dancer's life. The demands of practice and the need to continue lessons and to learn new routines and variations leave little time for recreational or social activities. As a career, dancing necessitates greater emphasis on self than on others; the intensive competition and the need to project oneself to get ahead leave little time for other pursuits.

Sources of Additional Information

■ **American Dance Guild**
31 West 21st Street, 3rd Floor
New York, NY 10010
Tel: 212-627-3790

■ **American Guild of Musical Artists**
1727 Broadway
New York, NY 10019
Tel: 212-265-3687

American Guild of Variety Artists
184 Fifth Avenue
New York, NY 10010
Tel: 212-675-1003

Canadian Dance Teachers Association
1123 McKeowan Avenue
North Bay, ON P1B 7M4 Canada

Choreographers Guild
256 South Robertson
Beverly Hills, CA 90211
Tel: 310-275-2573

Dance Educators of America
85 Rockaway Avenue
Rockville Center, NY 11570
Tel: 516-766-6615

National Dance Association
1900 Association Drive
Reston, VA 22091
Tel: 800-321-0789

Film and Television Directors

School Subjects
English (writing/literature), Theater/dance

Personal Interests
Film and Television, Photography

Work Environment
Indoors and outdoors, Primarily multiple locations

Minimum Education Level
Bachelor's degree

Salary Range
$35,000 to $500,000

Certification or Licensing
None

Outlook
Much faster than the average

DOT
143

GOE
01.02.03

NOC
5131

Definition

Lights! Camera! Action! aptly summarize the major responsibilities of the *film and television director.* In ultimate control of the decisions that shape a film or television production, the director is an artist who coordinates the elements of a film and is responsible for its overall style and quality.

Directors are well known for their part in guiding actors, but they are involved in much more—casting, costuming, cinematography, editing, and sound recording. Directors must have insight into the many tasks that go into the creation of a film, and they must have a broad vision of how each part will contribute to the big picture.

History

Greek playwrights and actors were tellers of tales, striving to impress and influence audiences with their dramatic interpretations of stories. That tradition continues today on stages and film screens throughout the world.

As far back as ancient Athens until some time in the nineteenth century, actors directed themselves. Although modern motion picture directors can find their roots in the theater, it wasn't until the mid-1880s that the director became someone other than a member of the acting cast. It had been common practice for one of the actors involved in a production to be responsible not only for his or her own performance but also for conducting rehearsals and coordinating the tasks involved in putting on a play. Usually the most experienced and respected troupe member would guide the other actors, providing advice on speech, movement, and interaction.

A British actress and opera singer named Madame Vestris is considered to have been the first professional director. In the 1830s Vestris leased a theater in London and staged productions in which she herself did not perform. She displayed a new, creative approach to directing, making bold decisions about changing traditional dress code for actors and allowing them to express their own interpretations of their roles. Vestris coordinated rehearsals, advised on lighting and sound effects, and chose nontraditional set decorations, introducing more realistic props (such as actual windows and doors) than the usual painted panoramas.

By the turn of the century, theater directors such as David Belasco (1859–1931) and Konstantin Stanislavsky (1863–1938) had influenced the way in which performances were given, provoking actors and actresses to strive to identify with the characters they revealed so that audiences would be passionately and genuinely affected. By the early 1900s, Stanislavsky's method of directing performers had made an overwhelming mark on drama. His method, as well as his famous criticism, "I do not believe you," continue to influence performers to this day.

At this same time, the motion picture industry was coming into being. European filmmakers such as Georges Melies and Leon Gaumont and New Yorker Edwin S. Porter were directing, filming, and producing minutes-long pictures. The industry's first professional female director was Alice Guy, who worked with Gaumont in the early years of the century. The technical sophistication offered by today's professionals was not part of the early directors' repertoire—they merely filmed narratives without moving their cameras. Soon directors began to experiment, moving the camera to shoot various angles and establishing a variety of editing techniques.

By 1915 there were close to 20,000 movie theaters in the United States; by the early 1920s, forty million people were going to Hollywood-produced and -directed silent movies every week.

Successful actors such as Charlie Chaplin (1889–1977) and Buster Keaton (1895–1966) began directing their own films, and Frank Capra (1897–1991) and Cecil B. deMille (1881–1959) were starting their long careers as professional directors.

With the emergence of "talking pictures" in the early 1930s, the director's role changed significantly. Sound in film provided opportunities for further directorial creativity. Unnecessary noise could not be tolerated on the set; directors had to be concerned with the voices of their performers and the potential sound effects that could be created. Directors could demand certain types of voices (e.g., a Southern drawl) and sound effects (e.g., the tatter of submachine guns) to present accurate interpretations of scripts. And no longer was the visually funny slapstick humor enough to make viewers laugh—professionals like Capra began directing successful comedies with sound.

The U.S. film industry experienced crises and controversy during the next fifty years, including financial problems, conglomerations of studios, and the introduction of the ratings system. New genres and elements began to challenge directorial genius over the years—science fiction, adventure, mystery; graphic representation of violence and sex; and sensational and computer-enhanced special effects. By the late 1970s university film schools were established and sending out creative directors—Francis Ford Coppola (born 1939), George Lucas (born 1944), Martin Scorsese (born 1942), and Steven Spielberg (born 1947), to name a few. Hollywood was reborn with the technical sophistication understood by these directors.

Nature of the Work

Motion picture directors, sometimes also called *filmmakers,* are considered ultimately responsible for the tone and quality of the films they work on. They interpret the stories and narratives presented in scripts and coordinate the filming of their interpretations. They are involved in preproduction, production, and postproduction. They audition, select, and rehearse the acting crew; they work on matters regarding set designs, musical scores, and costumes; and they decide on details such as where scenes should be shot, what backgrounds might be needed, and how special effects could be employed.

The director of a film often works with a *casting director,* who is in charge of auditioning performers. The casting director pays close attention to attributes of the performers like physical appearance, quality of voice, and acting ability and experience, and then presents to the director a list of suitable candidates for each role.

One of the most important aspects of the film director's job is working with the performers. Directors each have their own style in extracting accurate emotion and performance from cast members, but they must be dedicated to this goal.

Two common techniques that categorize directors' styles are montage and *mise-en-scene*. Montage directors are concerned with editing techniques to produce desired results; they consider it important to focus on how individual shots will work when pieced together with others. Consider Alfred Hitchcock (1899-1980), who directed the production of one scene in *Psycho*, for example, by filming discrete shots in a bathroom and then editing in dialogue, sound effects, and music to create tremendous suspense. *Mise-en-scene* directors are more concerned with the pre-editing phase, focusing on the elements of angles, movement, and design one shot at a time, as Orson Welles (1915–85) did. Many directors combine elements of both techniques in their work.

The film's *art director* creates set design concepts and chooses shoot locations. He or she meets with the filmmaker and producer to set budgets and schedules and then accordingly coordinates the construction of sets. Research is done on the period in which the film is to take place, and experts are consulted to help create appropriate architectural and environmental styles. The art director also is often involved in design ideas for costumes, makeup and hairstyles, photographic effects, and other elements of the film's production.

The *director of photography* is responsible for organizing and implementing the actual camera work. Together with the filmmaker, he or she interprets scenes and decides on appropriate camera motion to achieve desired results. The director of photography determines the amounts of natural and artificial lighting required for each shoot and such technical factors as the type of film to be used, camera angles and distance, depth of field, and focus.

Motion pictures are usually filmed out of sequence, meaning that the ending might be shot first and midscenes might not be filmed until the end of production. The director is responsible for scheduling each day's sequence of scenes; he or she coordinates filming so that scenes using the same set and performers will be filmed together. In addition to conferring with the art director and the director of photography, the filmmaker meets with technicians and crew members to advise on and approve final scenery, lighting, props, and other necessary equipment. He or she is also involved with final approval of costumes, choreography, and music.

After all the scenes have been shot, postproduction begins. The director works with picture and sound editors to cut apart and piece together the final reels. The *film editor* shares the director's vision about the picture and assembles shots according to that overall idea, synchronizing film with voice and sound tracks produced by the *sound editor* and *music editor.*

While the director supervises all major aspects of film production, various assistants help throughout the process. In a less creative position than the filmmaker, the *first assistant director* organizes various practical matters involved during the shooting of each scene. (This position is often erroneously considered a stepping stone to the director's chair.) The *second assistant director* is a coordinator who works as a liaison among the production office, the first assistant director, and the performers. The *second unit director* coordinates sequences such as scenics, inserts, and action shots that don't involve the main acting crew.

Requirements

Stanislavsky had a passion for his directorial work in the theater, believing that it was an art of immense social importance. Today's motion picture directors must have similar inspiration, if not greater creative strength because of the many more responsibilities involved in directing modern film. Film directors' careers are rather nontraditional. There is no standard training outline involved, no normal progression up a movie industry ladder leading to the director's job.

Dedication, talent, and experience have always been indispensable to a director. No doubt it is beneficial to become aware of one's passion for film as early as possible. Woody Allen (born 1935), for example, recognized the importance of motion pictures to him early in his life; but he worked as a magician, jazz clarinet player, joke writer, and stand-up comic before ever directing films. Allen took few film courses in his life.

On the other hand, many successful directors such as Francis Ford Coppola and Martha Coolidge have taken the formal film school route. There are more than five hundred film-studies programs offered by schools of higher education throughout the United States, including those considered to be the five most reputable: the American Film Institute (Los Angeles), Columbia University (New York.), New York University, the University of California at Los Angeles (UCLA), and the University of Southern California (USC). These schools have film professionals on their faculties and provide a very visible stage for student talent, being located in the two film-business hot spots—California and New York. (The tuition for film programs offered elsewhere, however, tends to be much less expensive than at these schools.)

Film school offers overall formal training, providing an education in fundamental directing skills by working with student productions. Such education is rigorous, but in addition to teaching skills it provides aspiring directors with peer groups and a network of contacts with students, faculty, and guest speakers that can be of help after graduation.

The debate continues on what is more influential in a directing career: film school or personal experience. Some say that it is always possible for people creative enough to land directing jobs without having gone through a formal program. Competition is so pervasive in the industry that even film school graduates find jobs scarce (only five to ten percent of the 26,000 students who graduate from film schools each year find jobs in the industry). Martha Coolidge, for instance, made independent films for ten years before directing a Hollywood movie.

Opportunities for Experience & Exploration

The most obvious opportunity for would-be directors lies in their own imaginations. Being drawn to films and captivated by the process of how they are made is the beginning of the filmmaker's journey.

In high school and beyond, pay attention to motion pictures—watch them at every opportunity, both at the theater and at home. Take an active part in school and community drama productions, whether as performer, set designer, or cue card holder. In college and afterward, take film classes and volunteer to work on other students' films. Two major trade publications to read are *Daily Variety* and *Hollywood Reporter*. Also, the book *How to Make It in Hollywood* (Linda Buzzell, 1992) is a very good informal guide that presents insider tips on such factors as "shmoozing" and *chutzpah* as well as an extensive list of valuable resources.

During summers, many camps and workshops offer programs for high school students interested in film work. For example, the University of Wisconsin offers its Summer Art Studio for students in grades seven through twelve; in addition to film courses, there are classes in other arts, such as drawing, painting, photography, and TV and video (for information, write to the University of Wisconsin–Green Bay, Office of Outreach, TH 335, Green Bay, WI 54311). UCLA presents its Media Workshops for students aged fourteen to twenty-four. Classes there focus on mass media production, including film, TV/video, and theater; sports activities, such as basketball, swimming, and tennis, are also offered (write to Media Workshops Foundation, UCLA, Rieber Hall, DeNeve Drive, Los Angeles, CA 90024).

Methods of Entering

It is considered difficult to enter a motion picture directorial position. With nontraditional steps to professional status, the occupation poses challenges for those seeking employment. However, there is somewhat solid advice for those who wish to direct motion pictures.

Many current directors began their careers in other film industry professions, such as acting or writing. Consider Jodie Foster, who appeared in thirty films before she went on to direct her first motion picture at the age of twenty-eight. Obviously it helps to grow up near the heart of "tinseltown" and to have the influence of one's family spurring you on. The support of family and friends is often cited as an essential element in shaping the confidence one needs to succeed in the industry.

As mentioned earlier, film school is a breeding ground for making contacts in the industry. Often, contacts are the essential factor in getting a job; many Hollywood insiders agree that it's not what you know but who you know that will get you in. Networking often leads to good opportunities at various types of jobs in the industry. Many professionals recommend that those who want to become directors should go to Los Angeles or New York, find any industry-related job, continue to take classes, and keep eyes and ears open for news of job openings, especially with those professionals who are admired for their talent.

A program to be aware of is the Assistant Directors Training Program of the Directors Guild of America (their address is listed below). This program provides an excellent opportunity to those without industry connections to work on film and television productions. Trainees are placed with major studios or on television movies and series. They work for four hundred days and earn between $424 and $521 per week, with the salary increasing every one hundred days. Once they have completed the program, they become freelance second assistant directors and can join the guild. The competition is extremely stiff for these positions; the program accepts only sixteen to twenty trainees from around fifteen hundred applicants each year.

Keep in mind that Hollywood isn't everything. Directors work on documentaries, on television productions, and with various types of video presentations, from music to business. Honing skills at these types of jobs is beneficial for those still intent on directing the big screen.

Advancement

In the motion picture industry, advancement often comes with recognition. Directors who work on well-received movies are given awards as well as further job offers. Probably the most glamorized trophy is the Academy Award of Merit—the Oscar. Sixteen Oscars, including one for Director of the Year, are given annually at a gala that recognizes the outstanding accomplishments of those in the field.

Candidates for Oscars are usually judged by their peers. Directors who have not worked on films popular enough to have made it in Hollywood should nevertheless seek recognition from reputable organizations. One such group is the National Endowment for the Arts, an independent agency of the U.S. government that supports and awards artists, including those who work in film. The endowment provides financial assistance in the form of fellowships and grants to those seen as contributing to the excellence of arts in the country.

Employment Outlook

According to the U.S. Department of Labor, employment for motion picture directors through the year 2005 is expected to grow much faster than the average for all occupations. This optimistic forecast is based on the increasing global demand for films made in the United States, as well as continuing U.S. demand for home video rentals.

However, competition is extreme and turnover is high. Most positions in the motion picture industry are held on a freelance basis. As is the case with most film industry workers, directors are usually hired to work on one film at a time. After a film is completed, new contacts must be made for further assignments.

Earnings

Directors' salaries vary greatly. Most Hollywood film directors are members of the Directors Guild of America, and salaries (as well as hours of work and other employment conditions) are usually negotiated by this union. Generally, contracts provide for minimum weekly salaries and follow a basic trend depending on the cost of the picture being produced: for film budgets over $1.5 million, the weekly salary is about $8,000; for budgets of $500,000—1.5 million, $5,800 per week; and for budgets under $500,000—$5,100. Motion picture art directors earn an average weekly salary of about $1,850; directors of photography, $2,000. Keep in mind that because directors are freelancers, they may have no income for many weeks out of the year.

Although contracts usually provide only for the minimum rate of pay, most directors earn more, and they often negotiate extra conditions. Woody Allen, for example, takes the minimum salary required by the union for directing a film but might also receive at least 10 percent of the film's gross receipts.

Conditions of Work

The work of the motion picture director is considered glamorous and prestigious, and of course directors have been known to become quite famous. But directors work under great stress—meeting deadlines, staying within budgets, and resolving problems among staff. "Nine-to-five" definitely does not describe a day in the life of a director; sixteen-hour days (and more) are not uncommon. And because directors are ultimately responsible for so much, schedules often dictate that they become immersed in their work around the clock, from preproduction to final cut. Nonetheless, this is the most enjoyable work to be found for those able to make it in the industry.

Sources of Additional Information

For information about colleges with film and television programs of study, please contact:

■ **American Film Institute**
PO Box 27999
2021 North Western Avenue
Los Angeles, CA 90027
Tel: 213-856-7600
WWW: http://www.afionline.org

■ **Broadcast Education Association**
1771 N Street, NW
Washington, DC 20036-2891
Tel: 202-429-5335
WWW: http://www.nab.org

For information about the Assistant Directors Training Program, please contact:

■ **Assistant Directors Training Program**
15503 Ventura Boulevard
Encino, CA 91436
Tel: 818-382-1744

For information about their Internship Directory or student membership, please contact:

■ **United States Institute of Theater Technology**
10 West 19th Street, Suite 5A
New York, NY 10011
Tel: 212-924-9088
WWW: http://www.culturenet.ca/usittenwriters

Film Editors

School Subjects
Art, English (writing/literature)

Personal Interests
Film and Television, Photography

Work Environment
Primarily indoors, Primarily one location

Minimum Education Level
High school diploma

Salary Range
$20,000 to $50,000

Certification or Licensing
None

Outlook
Faster than the average

DOT
962

GOE
01.01.01

NOC
5131

Definition

Film editors perform an essential role in the motion picture and television industries. They take an unedited draft of film or videotape and use specialized equipment to improve the draft until it is ready for viewing. It is the responsibility of the film editor to create the most effective film possible.

History

The motion picture and television industries have experienced substantial growth in the last few years in the United States. As more people have access to cable television, that industry has grown, too. The effect of this growth has been a steady demand for the essential skills that film editors provide. With recent innovations in computer technology, much of the work that film editors perform is accomplished using sophisticated computer programs. All of these factors have enabled many film editors to find steady work as salaried employees of film and television production companies and as independent contractors who provide their services on a per job basis.

Early film editing was sometimes done by directors, studio technicians, or others for whom this was not their specialty. Now every film, including the most brief television advertisement, has a film editor who is responsible for the continuity and clarity of the film.

Nature of the Work

Film editors work with producers and directors from the earliest phase of the project, called preproduction, and during the production phase, when actual filming occurs, through postproduction, which is when the film editor's skills are in greatest demand. During preproduction, in meetings with producers, the film editor learns about the objectives of the film. If it is an advertisement, for example, the film editor must be familiar with the product the film will attempt to sell. If the project is a feature-length motion picture, the film editor must understand the story line. The producer may explain the larger scope of the project so that the film editor knows the best way to approach the work when it is his or her time to edit the film. In consultation with the director, the film editor may discuss the best way to accurately present the screenplay or script. He or she may discuss different settings, scenes, or camera angles even before filming begins. With this kind of preparation, the film editor will be ready to practice his or her craft as soon as the production phase is complete.

Feature-length films, of course, take much more time to edit than television commercials. Therefore, some film editors may spend months on one project, while others may be working on several shorter films simultaneously.

Film editors assess all of the film segments as they arrive from the camera operators. The film editors are usually the final decision-makers when it comes to choosing which segments will stay in the film, which segments will be cut, or which may need to be redone. The film editor looks at the quality of the film segment, its dramatic value, and its relationship to other segments. The film editor then arranges the segments in an order that creates the most effective finished product. In commercials, which typically run for between fifteen and sixty seconds, the film editor must arrange the segments to comply with these time limitations.

The editing equipment that a film editor may use varies from one studio to another. Some studios and postproduction companies still have their film editors cut and splice film with razor blades and special tape. Others perform these tasks using sophisticated computer programs. At most studios and postproduction companies, film editors review the assembled film segments on video monitors. At this point the director usually reviews the film with the film editor and participates in making decisions about timing, placement, or order of the segments.

Some film editors specialize in certain areas of television or film. *Sound editors* work on the soundtracks of television programs or motion pictures. They often keep libraries of sounds that they reuse for various projects. These include natural sounds such as thunder or raindrops, animal noises, motor sounds, or musical interludes. Some sound editors specialize in music and may have training in music theory or performance. Others work with sound effects. They may use unusual objects, machines, or computer-generated noisemakers to create a desired sound for a film.

Some film editors work primarily with news programs, documentaries, or special features. They may develop ongoing working relationships with directors or producers who hire them from one project to another.

Many film editors who have worked for a studio or postproduction company for several years often become independent contractors. They offer their services on a per job basis to producers of films and advertisements, negotiating their own fees, and typically have purchased or leased their own editing equipment.

Requirements

Some studios require a bachelor's degree for those seeking positions as film editors, yet actual on-the-job experience is the best guarantee of securing lasting employment. Degrees in liberal-arts fields are preferred, but courses in cinematography and audiovisual techniques help film editors get started in their work. Liberal-arts educations are available at four-year colleges, universities, and some two-year colleges.

Training as a film editor takes from four to ten years. Many film editors learn much of their work on the job. Some two-year colleges offer film editing courses. Training in film editing is also available in the military, including the air force, marine corps, coast guard, and navy.

Opportunities for Experience & Exploration

Many high schools have film clubs, and some have cable television stations affiliated with the school district. These are good places for those interested in a career as a film editor to get experience. Often school-run television channels give students the opportunity to actually create and edit short programs.

The best way to prepare for a career as a film editor is to read widely. High school English classes, as well as later college literature classes, help future film editors learn to think critically. In reading literature, students get a sense of the different ways in which stories can be presented. Some high schools even offer film classes. Community colleges and universities may offer seminars for students or present lectures by broadcasters that are open to the public.

Film editors should be familiar with all different kinds of films, including documentary and nonfictional films, educational films, and dramatic or fictional films. Each kind of film requires a different type of editing. Transitions in most fictional films, for example, are very smooth and subtle, while those in documentaries or news films are often sharp and fast-paced.

Large television stations and film companies occasionally have volunteers or student interns. It is possible to get a position helping in a film studio—even doing menial tasks—so that one may later get an apprenticeship with a film editor. Most people in the film industry start out doing minor tasks helping with production. These *production assistants* get the opportunity to see all of the different people and tasks required in the creation of a motion picture or television broadcast. By working closely with a film editor, a production assistant can learn television or film operations as well as specific film editing techniques.

Methods of Entering

With a minimum of a high school diploma or a degree from a two-year college, an interested applicant can apply for entry-level jobs in many film or television studios. Most studios, however, will not consider people for film editor positions without a bachelor's degree or several years of on-the-job experience. Larger studios may offer apprenticeships for film editors. In the apprenticeship, an apprentice has the opportunity to see the work of the film editor up close. The film editor may eventually assign some of his or her minor duties to the apprentice, while the film editor makes the larger decisions. After a few years the apprentice may be promoted to film editor or may apply for a position as a film editor at other studios.

Some sound or sound-effects editors may wish to broaden their skills by working as general film editors. Some film editors may, on the other hand, choose to specialize in sound effects, music, or some other editorial area. Some film editors who work in television may move to motion pictures or may move from working on commercials or television series to television movies.

Advancement

Once film editors have secured employment in their field, their advancement comes with further experience and greater recognition. Some film editors develop good working relationships with directors or producers. These film editors may be willing to leave the security of a studio job for the possibility of working one-on-one with the director or producer on a project. These opportunities often provide film editors with the autonomy they may not get in their regular jobs. Some are willing to take a pay cut to work on a project they feel is important.

Some film editors choose to stay at their studios and advance through seniority to editing positions with higher salaries. They may be able to negotiate better benefits packages or to choose the films they will work on. They may also choose which directors they wish to work with. In larger studios they may train and supervise staffs of less experienced or apprentice film editors.

Employment Outlook

The outlook for film editors is good. The growth of cable television and an increase in the number of independent film studios will translate into greater demand for film editors. This will also force the largest studios to offer more competitive salaries in order to attract the best film editors. More jobs should be opening in the field, and film editors should be able to find positions despite the high level of competition.

Earnings

Film editors are not as highly paid as others working in the film or television industries. They have less clout than directors or producers, although they have more authority in the production of a film than many other film technicians. In the 1990s the minimum weekly salary for a film editor is about $1,400. The minimum weekly salary for an assistant film editor is about $1,000, and the minimum for a sound effects or music editor is about $960. A film or tape editor working in television broadcasting earns about $20,000 annually. The most experienced and sought-after film editors can command higher salaries.

Conditions of Work

Most of the work done by film editors is done in film studios or at postproduction companies using editing equipment. The working environment is often a small, cramped studio office. Working hours vary widely depending on the film. During the filming of a commercial, for instance, film editors may be required to work overtime, at night, or on weekends to finish the project by an assigned date. Many feature-length films are kept on tight production schedules that allow for steady work unless filming gets behind.

During filming, film editors may be asked to be on hand at the filming location. Locations may be outdoors or in other cities, and travel is occasionally required. More often, however, the film editor edits in the studio, and that is where the bulk of the film editor's time is spent.

Disadvantages of the film editor's job involve the editor's low rank on the totem pole of film or television industry jobs. However, most film editors feel that this is outweighed by the advantages. Film editors can view the films on which they have worked and be proud of their role in creating them.

Sources of Additional Information

■ **American Cinema Editors**
4416 Finley Avenue
Los Angeles, CA 90027
Tel: 213-850-2900

■ **American Film Institute**
John F. Kennedy Center for the Performing Arts
Washington, DC 20566
Tel: 202-828-4000

■ **Foundation of Independent Video and Filmmakers**
625 Broadway, 9th Floor
New York, NY 10012
Tel: 212-473-3400

Graphic Designers

School Subjects
Art, Computer science

Personal Interests
Computers, Drawing/painting

Work Environment
Primarily indoors, Primarily one location

Minimum Education Level
Some postsecondary training

Salary Range
$17,000 to $50,000+

Certification or Licensing
None

Outlook
Faster than the average

DOT
141

GOE
01.02.03

NOC
5241

Definition

Graphic designers are practical artists whose creations are intended to express ideas, convey information, or draw attention to a product. They design a wide variety of materials including advertisements, displays, packaging, signs, computer graphics and games, book and magazine covers and interiors, animated characters, and company logos to fit the needs and preferences of their various clients.

History

The history of graphic design as an applied art parallels that of fine art. In every age, examples of practical art can be found alongside paintings and sculpture. Many modern graphic designers can trace the beginnings of their art through history.

Computer technology of the twentieth century has revolutionized many government, business, and private operations. It has also changed the way many graphic designers do their work: today it is possible to be a successful graphic designer even if you can't draw more than simple stick figures. With the invention of computer chips that can store billions of pieces of information, graphic designers are able to draw, color, and revise the many different images they work with daily. Computer graphics enable graphic designers to work more quickly, since details like size, shape, and color are easy to change.

Graphics programs for computers are continually revised and improved, moving more and more design work from the artist's table to the computer mousepad and graphics tablet. This area of computer technology is a hot spot now and will be in the future, as computer graphics and multimedia move toward virtual reality applications. Many graphic designers with solid computer experience will be needed to work with these systems.

The challenge of combining beauty, function, and technology in whatever form has preoccupied artisans in all periods of history. Graphic design work has been used to create products and promote commerce for as long as people have used symbols, characters, or letters of an alphabet. Only the formal aspect of graphic design occupations is relatively modern.

Nature of the Work

Graphic designers are not primarily fine artists, although they may be highly skilled at drawing or painting. Most designs commissioned to graphic designers involve both artwork and copy (that is, words). Thus, the designer must not only be familiar with the wide range of art media (photography, drawing, painting, collage, etc.) and styles, but he or she must also be familiar with a wide range of typefaces and know how to manipulate them for the right effect. Because design tends to change in a similar way to fashion, designers must keep up to date with the latest trends and hot looks. At the same time, they must be well grounded in more traditional, classic designs. Graphic designers can work as in-house designers for a particular company, as staff designers for a graphic design firm, or as freelance designers working for themselves. Some designers specialize in designing advertising materials or packaging; others focus on "corporate identity" materials such as company stationery and logos; others work mainly for publishers designing book and magazine covers and page layouts; others work in the area of computer graphics, creating still or animated graphics for computer software, videos, or motion pictures. A highly specialized type of graphic designer, the environmental graphic designer, designs large outdoor signs. Some graphic designers design exclusively on the computer, while others may use both the computer and traditional hand drawings or paintings, depending on the project's needs and requirements.

Whatever the specialty and whatever their medium, all graphic designers take a similar approach to a project, whether it is for an entirely new design or for a variation on an existing one. Graphic designers begin by determining as best they can the needs and preferences of the clients and the potential users, buyers, or viewers.

In the case of a graphic designer working on a company logo, for example, he or she will likely meet with company representatives to discuss such points as how and where the company is going to use the logo and what size, color, and shape preferences company executives might have. Project budgets must be carefully respected: a design that may be perfect in every way but that is too costly to reproduce is basically useless. Graphic designers may need to compare their ideas with similar ones from other companies and analyze the image they project. Thus they must have a good knowledge of how various colors, shapes, and layouts affect the viewer psychologically.

After a plan has been conceived and the details worked out, the graphic designer does some preliminary designs (generally two or three) to present to the client for approval. The client may reject the preliminary design entirely and request a new design, or he or she may ask the designer to make alterations to the existing design. The designer then goes "back to the drawing board" to attempt a new design or make the requested changes. This process continues until the client approves the design.

Once a design has been approved, the graphic designer prepares the design for professional reproduction, that is, printing. The printer may require a "mechanical," in which the artwork and copy are arranged on a white board just as it is to be photographed, or the designer may be asked to submit an electronic copy of the design. Either way, designers must have a good understanding of the printing process, including color separation, paper properties, and halftone (i.e., photographs) reproduction.

Requirements

As with all artists, graphic designers need a degree of artistic talent, creativity, and imagination. They must be sensitive to beauty and have an eye for detail and a strong sense of color, balance, and proportion. To a great extent, these qualities are natural, but they can be developed through training, both on the job and in professional schools, colleges, and universities.

More and more graphic designers need solid computer skills and working knowledge of several of the common drawing, image editing, and page layout programs. Graphic design on the computer is more commonly done on a Macintosh system than on a PC system; however many designers have both types of computers.

More graphic designers are recognizing the value of formal training, and at least two out of three people entering the field today have a college degree or some college education. Over one hundred colleges and art schools offer graphic design programs that are accredited by the National Association of Schools of Art and Design. At many schools, graphic design students must take a year of basic art and design courses before being accepted into the bachelor's degree program. In addition, applicants to the bachelor's degree programs in graphic arts may be asked to submit samples of their work to prove artistic ability. Many schools and employers depend on samples, or portfolios, to evaluate the applicants' skills in graphic design. Many programs increasingly emphasize the importance of using computers for design work. Computer proficiency among graphic designers will be very important in the years to come. Interested individuals should select an academic program that incorporates computer training into the curriculum, or train themselves on their own.

A bachelor of fine arts program at a four-year college or university may include courses such as principles of design, art and art history, painting, sculpture, mechanical and architectural drawing, architecture, computerized design, basic engineering, fashion designing and sketching, garment construction, and textiles. Such degrees are desirable but not always necessary for obtaining a position as a graphic designer.

With or without specialized education, graphic designers seeking employment should have a good portfolio containing samples of their best work. The graphic designer's portfolio is extremely important and can make a difference when an employer must choose between two otherwise equally qualified candidates.

A period of on-the-job training is expected for all beginning designers. The length of time it takes to become fully qualified as a graphic designer may run from one to three years, depending on prior education and experience as well as innate talent.

Opportunities for Experience & Exploration

High school students interested in a career in graphic design have a number of ways to find out whether they have the talent, ambition, and perseverance to succeed in the field. Students should take as many art and design courses as possible while still in high school and should become proficient at working on computers. In addition, to get an insider's view of various design occupations, they could enlist the help of art teachers or school guidance counselors to make arrangements to tour design companies and interview designers.

While studying, students interested in graphic design can get practical experience by participating in school and community projects that call for design talents. These might include such activities as building sets for plays, setting up exhibits, planning seasonal and holiday displays, and preparing programs and other printed materials. For those interested in publication design, work on the school newspaper or yearbook is invaluable.

Part-time and summer jobs offer would-be designers an excellent way to become familiar with the day-to-day requirements of a particular design occupation and gain some basic related experience. Possible places of employment include design studios, design departments in advertising agencies and manufacturing companies, department and furniture stores, flower shops, workshops that produce ornamental items, and museums. Museums also use a number of volunteer workers. Inexperienced people are often employed as sales, clerical, or general helpers; those with a little more education and experience may qualify for jobs in which they have a chance to develop actual design skills and build portfolios of completed design projects.

Methods of Entering

The best way to enter the field of graphic design is to have a strong portfolio. Potential employers rely on portfolios to evaluate talent and how that talent might be used to fit the company's special needs. Beginning graphic designers can assemble a portfolio from work completed at school, in art classes, and in part-time or freelance jobs. The portfolio should continually be updated to reflect the designer's growing skills, so it will always be ready for possible job changes.

Job interviews may be obtained by applying directly to companies that employ designers. Many colleges and professional schools have placement services to help their graduates find positions, and sometimes it is possible to get a referral from a previous part-time employer or volunteer coordinator.

Advancement

As part of their on-the-job training, beginning graphic designers generally are given the simpler tasks and work under direct supervision. As they gain experience, they move up to more complex work with increasingly less supervision.

Experienced graphic designers, especially those with leadership capabilities, may be promoted to *chief designer, design department head,* or other supervisory positions.

Computer graphic designers can move into other computer-related positions with additional education. Some may become interested in graphics programming in order to further improve computer design capabilities. Others may want to become involved with multimedia and interactive graphics. Video games, touch-screen displays in stores, and even laser light shows are all products of multimedia graphic designers.

When designers develop personal styles that are in high demand in the marketplace, they sometimes go into business for themselves. Freelance design work can be erratic, however, so usually only the most experienced designers with an established client base can count on consistent full-time work.

Employment Outlook

Chances for employment look very good for qualified graphic designers through the year 2005, especially for those involved with computer graphics. The design field in general is expected to grow at a faster than average rate. As computer graphic technology continues to advance, there will be a need for well-trained computer graphic designers. Companies that have always used graphics will expect their designers to perform work on computers. Companies for which graphic design was once too time consuming or costly are now sprucing up company newsletters and magazines, among other things, and need graphic designers to do it.

Because the design field is a popular one, appealing to many talented individuals, competition is expected to be strong in all areas. Beginners and designers with only average talent or without formal education and technical skills may encounter some difficulty in securing employment.

About one-third of all graphic designers are self-employed, a higher proportion than is found in most other occupations. Salaried designers work in many different industries, including the wholesale and retail trade (department stores, furniture and home furnishings stores, apparel stores, florist shops); manufacturing industries (machinery, motor vehicles and aircraft, metal products, instruments, apparel, textiles, printing and publishing); service industries (business services, engineering, architecture); construction firms; and government agencies. Public relations and publicity firms, advertising agencies, commercial printers, and mail-order houses all have graphic design departments.

Earnings

The range of salaries for graphic designers is quite broad. Many earn as little as $17,000, while others receive more than $35,000. Salaries depend primarily on the nature and scope of the employer, with computer graphic designers earning wages on the high end of the range.

Self-employed designers can earn a lot one year and substantially more or less the next. Their earnings depend on individual talent and business ability, but, in general, are higher than those of salaried designers, although like any self-employed individual, they must pay their own insurance costs and taxes and are not compensated for vacation or sick days.

Salaried designers who advance to the position of design manager or design director earn about $60,000 a year and, at the level of corporate vice-president, make $70,000 and up. The owner of a consulting firm can make $85,000 or more.

Graphic designers who work for large corporations receive full benefits, including health insurance, paid vacation, and sick leave.

Conditions of Work

Most graphic designers work regular hours in clean, comfortable, pleasant offices or studios. Conditions vary depending on the design specialty.

Some graphic designers work in small establishments with few employees; others, in large organizations with large design departments. Some deal mostly with their co-workers; others may have a lot of public contact. Freelance designers are paid by the assignment. To maintain a steady income, they must constantly strive to please their clients and to find new ones.

Computer graphic designers may have to work long, irregular hours in order to complete an especially ambitious project.

Sources of Additional Information

■ **American Center for Design**
233 East Ontario, Suite 500
Chicago, IL 60611
Tel: 312-787-2018

For more information about careers in graphic design, contact:

■ **American Institute of Graphic Arts**
164 Fifth Avenue
New York, NY 10160-1652
Tel: 800-548-1634
Email: aiganatl@aol.com

■ **National Association of Schools of Art and Design**
11250 Roger Bacon Drive, Suite 21
Reston, VA 22090
Tel: 703-437-0700

■ **Society for Environmental Graphic Design**
1 Story Street
Cambridge, MA 02138
Tel: 617-868-3381

■ **Society of Publication Designers**
60 East 42nd Street, Suite 721
New York, NY 10165
Tel: 212-983-8585

■ **Urban Art International**
PO Box 868
Tiburon, CA 94920
Tel: 415-435-5767
WWW: http://wwwhite.imagesite.com

Musical Directors and Conductors

School Subjects
Music, Theater/dance

Personal Interests
Entertaining, Music

Work Environment
Primarily indoors, Primarily one location

Minimum Education Level
High school diploma

Salary Range
$15,000 to $500,000+

Certification or Licensing
None

Outlook
Little change or more slowly than the average

DOT
152

GOE
01.04.01

NOC
5131

Definition

Musical conductors direct large groups of musicians or singers in the performance of a piece of music. There are various types of conductors, including those who lead symphony orchestras, dance bands, marching bands, and choral groups. They use their hands, a baton, or both to indicate the musical sound variations and timing of a composition. Their chief concern is their interpretation of how a piece of music should be played. They are responsible for rehearsing the orchestra and auditioning musicians for positions in the ensemble.

Conductors must have the complete respect of the musicians they lead. The great conductors have a personal charisma that awes both musician and listener alike. Conductors are unique in the modern musical world in that they make no sound themselves, yet control the sound that others make. The orchestra is their instrument. Musical conductors sometimes carry the title of *musical director*, which implies a wider area of responsibilities, including administrative and managerial duties.

History

The origins of musical conducting remain quite obscure. Some form of time keeping undoubtedly went on even among primitive musical groups. In early orchestral days time beating was often done orally, with the use of a scroll, or by pounding a long stick on the floor. During the eighteenth century a musician often kept time, usually the organist or harpsichordist or the chief of the first violinists, who came to be called the "concertmaster." There were no specialist conductors at this time; the composer generally served as the conductor, and he usually conducted only his own works. The concertmaster role grew increasingly more important, and for a period it was not unusual for him to keep time by stamping his feet even when there was a separate conductor who might also keep time by clapping his hands or tapping a desk. Needless to say, this simultaneous stamping and clapping could be very irritating to musicians and audience alike.

Just when the baton was first used is not known, but mention of using a staff in this manner was made in Greek mythology as early as 709 BCE. It is known that batons were used since the eighth century and became fashionable, as orchestras grew larger, in the late eighteenth century. By the mid-nineteenth century their usage was a widely accepted practice.

In 1776, *Kapellmeister* Johann Reichardt conducted the Berlin Court Opera with a baton, possibly the first to do so. Early in the nineteenth century, Ludwig Spohr (1784–1859) was perhaps the first musician to be recognized purely as a conductor and was another of the early users of the baton rather than the bow or a paper scroll. The baton was at first a rather large and awkward device similar to the instrument used by a drum major. Hector Berlioz (1803–69) used such a baton in his white-gloved hand, while Felix Mendelssohn (1808–47) used a scroll or a stick; the latter was particularly notable for the grandeur of his style. Mendelssohn also regularly cut and reorchestrated the compositions he conducted, a practice that has continued. Some conductors of the period eschewed the baton and used their bare hands. This practice was never widely adopted, although a few great conductors, including Leopold Stokowski (1882–1977), preferred the bare hand method.

Berlioz was one of the great early nineteenth century composer-conductors who influenced conducting style into the next century. Among the other major influences were Felix Mendelssohn and Richard Wagner (1813–83). These men assumed full, autocratic command of the orchestra, each insisting on strict obedience from the musicians in carrying out the conductor's interpretation of the music. Gustav Mahler (1860–1911), in the late nineteenth century, wielded a tyrannical power over the orchestra and flew into rages that became legendary. Many different conducting styles emerged in the twentieth century, including some that were highly exhibitionistic. Leopold Stokowski and Leonard Bernstein (1918–90) have also been noted for their dramatic exhibitionism. In the early 1920s in Russia an attempt was made at forming a conductorless orchestra, undoubtedly to eliminate the dictatorial rule of the conductor. The experiment died out after a few years, although in the late 1920s conductorless experiments were attempted in New York City and Budapest.

The outstanding conductors in the twentieth century are too numerous to mention, but one name is perhaps legendary above all others. This would be Arturo Toscanini (1867–1957), originally an opera composer, whose infallible ear, musicianship, comprehensive knowledge of scores, and orchestral control made him virtually the prototype of great twentieth-century conductors. At rehearsals his famed temper flared as he exhorted his charges to perfectly perform his interpretation of a score. Before the audience he exuded charisma. Toscanini, who conducted the New York Philharmonic Symphony from 1928 to 1936 and the NBC Symphony from 1937 to 1954, was perhaps the most influential conductor of the mid-twentieth century, his main rival being Furtwangler in Germany. Some conductors of the late twentieth century, however, remained free of both influences. Perhaps the most notable of these was Sir Georg Solti (1912–1997), who with large and seemingly awkward movements inspired his musicians to brilliant heights of musical perfection. Many authorities acknowledge that through his guidance the Chicago Symphony Orchestra has become the finest musical ensemble of the late twentieth century. While many women have taken their places among the great orchestras of the world, few have been able to move into the field of conducting. In the second half of the twentieth century, however, there were some breakthroughs, and a number of women conductors such as Sarah Caldwell in the United States achieved recognition.

Nature of the Work

Conducting—whether it be of a symphony orchestra, an opera, a chorus, a theater pit orchestra, a marching band, or even a "big" swing band—is an enormously complex and demanding occupation to which only the exceptional individual can possibly aspire with hope of even moderate success. A conductor must have multiple skills and talents. First and foremost he must be a consummate musician. Not only should he have mastered an instrument himself (he may have come from the orchestra or been a piano recitalist), but he also must know music and be able to interpret the score of any composition he is required to play. His ear should be unerring. He must have an uncommon bearing that commands the respect of the musicians. He must display an air of authority and confidence that makes him the unqualified leader of the orchestra, while displaying no weakness or indecisiveness that would weaken his command. At the same time the conductor needs to be sensitive to the musicians and sympathetic to their problems; he should be able to inspire the musicians as well as bring out the very best they have to offer. Conductors must also have a sense of showmanship. Some conductors have advanced farther than others because their dramatic conducting style helps bring in larger audiences and greater receipts. The conductor must also be a psychologist who can deal with the multiplicity of complex and temperamental personalities presented by a large ensemble of musicians and singers. Conductors must exude personal charm; orchestras are always fund-raising, and the conductor is frequently expected to meet major donors to keep their good will. Finally, and in line with fund-raising, conductors are expected to have administrative skills and to understand the business and financial problems that face the orchestra organization.

Conductors are distinguished by their baton technique and arm and body movements. These can vary widely from conductor to conductor, some being reserved and holding to minimal movements, others using sweeping baton strokes and broad arm and body gestures. There is no right or wrong way to conduct; it is a highly individualized art, and great conductors produce excellent results using extremely contrasting styles. The conductor's fundamental purpose in leading, regardless of style, is to set the tempo and rhythm of a piece. Conductors must be sure that the orchestra is following their interpretation of the music, and they must resolve any problems that the score poses. Failure to render a composition in a way that is pleasing to the public and the critics is usually blamed on the conductor, although there is a school that feels that both the conductor and the musicians are to blame, or that at least it is difficult to tell which one is most at fault.

The quality of a performance is probably most directly related to the conductor's rehearsal techniques. It is during rehearsals that conductors must diagnose and correct to their satisfaction the musical, interpretive, rhythmic, balance, and intonation problems encountered by the orchestra. They must work with each unit of the orchestra individually and the entire ensemble as a whole; this may include soloist instrumentalists and singers as well as a chorus. Some conductors rehearse every detail of a score while others have been known to emphasize only certain parts during rehearsal. Some are quiet and restrained at rehearsals, while others work to a feverish emotional pitch.

The sound that an orchestra makes is also identified with the conductor, and for some, such as Eugene Ormandy (1899–1985), formerly of the Philadelphia Orchestra, the tone of an orchestra becomes a recognizable signature. Tone is determined by the conductor's use of the various sections of the orchestra. The brass section, for instance, can be instructed to play so that the sound is bright, sharp, and piercing, or they can play to produce a rich, sonorous, and heavy sound. The strings can play the vibrato broadly to produce a thick, lush tone or play with little vibrato to produce a thinner, more delicate sound.

While few people have the makeup required to be a conductor, there are many situations in which conductors may work. Music teachers in schools often take on conducting as a natural extension of their duties. Conservatories and institutions of higher learning frequently have fine orchestras, choruses, and bands that often choose conductors from the faculty. There are numerous summer festivals that employ conductors, and conductors may also find positions with community orchestras and choruses, local opera companies, and musical theater groups; even amateur groups sometimes hire outside conductors. For the very exceptional, of course, there is the possibility of conducting with famous orchestra, theater, and opera companies, as well as the musical groups associated with broadcasting and film studios. Well-known conductors are in demand and they travel a great deal, appearing as a guest conductor with other orchestras or making personal appearances.

Requirements

It was once commonly thought that conducting was unteachable. That attitude has been changing, however, and some institutions have developed formalized programs to teach the art of conducting. The Paris Conservatory is particularly noted for its conducting instruction, and completion of that institution's course is said to pave the way to opportunities in conducting. The Julliard School is another institution known for its studies in conducting. Still, many conductors performing today have had little or no formalized instruction.

As indicated above, conductors must acquire a multiplicity of skills in order to practice their art. These skills may be divided into three parts: technical skills, performance skills, and conducting skills.

Technical skills deal with conductors' ability to control orchestral intonation, balance, and color; they must be advanced at sight-reading and transposition in order to cope with orchestral scores. Conductors must acquire a comprehensive knowledge of all orchestral instruments and must themselves have mastery of at least one instrument, the piano probably being the most helpful. They must acquire skills in composition and musical analysis, which presumes accomplished skills in counterpoint, harmony, musical structures, and orchestration. Finally, conductors must understand and be able to adapt musical styling.

Performance skills refer to conductors' own instrumental ability. Mastery of one instrument is important, but the more instruments conductors know, the better they will be able to relate to members of the orchestra. It is through knowledge of instruments that conductors develop their interpretive abilities.

Conducting skills involve the ability to use the baton and to control the timing, rhythm, and structure of a musical piece. Conductors must develop these skills at performances and at rehearsals. At rehearsals they must use their power and their intellect to blend the various elements of the orchestra and the composition into a single unified presentation. Conductors must also learn to use their whole bodies, along with the baton, to control the music.

Conductors require not only an extensive knowledge of music but also a strong general background in the arts and humanities as well. They should have a comprehensive knowledge of musical history as it fits into the general fabric of civilization along with competence in various languages, including French, German, Italian, and Latin. Language skills are particularly helpful in coaching singers. Familiarity with the history of Western civilization, particularly its literature, drama, and art will also be valuable in the composer's musical frame of reference.

Conductors also require a high degree of self-discipline and unquestioned integrity in order to fill a difficult and complex leadership role. It is important as well that they learn all the aspects of the business and social functions of an orchestra.

As indicated above, conductors are very special people. Like musicians and composers, they must have talent, a quality that cannot be taught or acquired. Conductors, however, require even more intangibles to practice their art. They must have supreme self-confidence in their ability to lead and interpret the music of the great masters. They must convince both audience and ensemble that they are in command. To accomplish all of this, conductors must have another quality that is even more difficult to define: charisma. Through this quality, inborn or somehow acquired, as the case may be, conductors can perform the Herculean feat of bringing many different instruments, voices, and personalities together at one time and place to create a presentation of artistic beauty.

Opportunities for Experience & Exploration

The best way to become familiar with the art of conducting is to study music and the great conductors themselves. It is not possible to understand conducting beyond the most superficial level without a good background in music. Students of conducting should go to as many musical presentations as they can—symphonies, operas, musical theater, and the like—and study the conductors; note their baton techniques and their arm and body movements. They should try to determine how the orchestra and audience respond to the gesturing of the conductors. There are also any number of associations, reference books, and biographies that can provide detailed information about conductors and their art. One of the most prominent organizations is the American Symphony Orchestra League located in Washington, DC. They hold a national conference and conducting workshops each year. Useful books that deal with conducting include *Handbook of Conducting* by Herman Scherchen, *The Great Conductors* by Harold Schonberg, *Exploring Careers in Music* by Judith Feder, *A History of Orchestral Conducting in Theory and Practice* by Elliott W. Galkin, *The Grammar of Conducting* by Max Rudolf, and *Conductors in Conversation: Fifteen Contemporary Conductors Discuss Their Lives and Profession* by Jeannine Wagar.

Methods of Entering

It is unlikely that many people start out at a very early point in life to become a musical conductor. Most conductors begin at an early age studying music and possibly, at some later point in life, discover or suspect that they have the qualities to become a conductor. Some conductors become involved at the high school or college level leading a small group for whom they may also do the arranging and possibly some composing. There are some courses specifically in conducting at advanced institutions, and interested students may take courses in composition, arranging, and orchestrating, which provide a good background for conducting. Some opportunities to conduct may arise at university, and it is sometimes possible for aspiring conductors to study with a faculty member who conducts the school orchestra. There are also conductor training programs and apprenticeship programs that may be applied for, which are announced in the music trade papers and in reference sources such as *Musical America: International Directory of the Performing Arts*.

A career in conducting begins with a sound musical education. Working as an instrumentalist in an orchestral group under a good conductor whose technique can be studied is an important step toward conducting. The piano is an important instrument for the conductors to know, because it will not only enable them to score and arrange more easily, it also will be useful in coaching singers, which many conductors do as a sideline, and in rehearsing an orchestra as assistant conductor. That is not to say, however, that other instrumentalists do not also acquire a good background for conducting.

With a solid foundation in musical education and some experience with an orchestra, young conductors should seek any way possible to acquire experience conducting. To begin with, there are many grants and fellowships that can be applied for, and many summer music festivals advertise for conductors. Often these situations present the opportunity to work or study under a famous conductor who has been engaged to oversee or administer a festival. Such experience is invaluable because it provides opportunities to make contacts for various other conducting positions. These may include apprenticeships, jobs with university choirs and orchestras (which may include a faculty position), or opportunities with community orchestras, small opera companies, or amateur groups that seek a professional music director. Experience in these positions can lead to offers with major orchestras, opera, or musical theater companies as assistant or associate conductor.

Not everyone will want or be able to move into a major role as conductor of a well-known orchestra. Many, in fact most, will remain in the lesser jobs that have been listed already. Those seeking to further their career as a conductor may want to invest in a personal manager who will find bookings and situations for ambitious young talent. Entering the conducting field will take more of an investment than most other careers. Musical education, applying for grants and fellowships, and attending workshops and summer music camps and festivals can add up to a considerable expense. Moving into a good conducting job may take time as well, and young people going into the field should not expect to reach the pinnacle of their profession until they are well into their thirties or forties or even older—if ever.

Advancement

There is no real hierarchy in an orchestra organization that one can climb to the role of conductor. The most likely advancement within an organization would be from the position of assistant or associate conductor or from that of the head first violinist—i.e., the concertmaster. Conductors generally move from smaller conducting jobs to larger ones. A likely advancement would be from a small community orchestra or youth orchestra (probably a part-time position), to a small city orchestra (full or part-time), and from there to a larger city orchestra, a mid-size opera company, or directorship of a middle-level television or film company. Such advancement presumes that the conductor has had sufficient recognition and quality reviews to come to the attention of the larger musical groups.

Conductors who take the leadership of mid-size city orchestras and opera companies may by that point be in the hands of an agent or manager, who takes care of financial matters, guest bookings, and personal appearances. The agent will also be looking for advancement to more prestigious conducting jobs in the larger cities. At the point that conductors receive national or international recognition it becomes a question of which major position they will accept as openings occur. It is unlikely that a major city orchestra would promote someone within the organization when the conductorship is open. It is more probable that a search committee will conduct an international search to find a "big name" conductor for the post. Conductors themselves can advance to top-level administrative positions, such as artistic director or executive director.

Employment Outlook

The operating cost for an orchestra continues to grow every year, and musical organizations are in constant budget-trimming modes as have been most other professional business organizations in the 1990s. This has tended to affect growth in the orchestra field, and, accordingly, the number of conducting jobs. Additionally, the overall number of orchestras in the United States has grown only slightly in the last two decades. The number of orchestras in academia declined slightly while the community, youth, and city orchestras for the most part gained slightly in number. The slight growth pattern of orchestra groups will not nearly accommodate the number of people who graduated from music school during that period and are trying to become conductors. The competition for conducting jobs, already tight, will become even tighter in the next decade. Only the most talented people moving into the field will be able to find full-time jobs.

Earnings

It is difficult to estimate the earnings of conductors. The range is enormous, and there is variation from one category of conductors to another. For instance, many conductors work only part time and make quite small yearly incomes for their conducting endeavors. Part-time choir directors for churches and temples, for instance, make from $3,500 to $25,000 per year, while full-time directors make from $15,000 to $40,000 per year. Conductors of dance bands make from $300 to $1,200 per week. Opera and choral group conductors make as little as $8,000 per year working part time at the community level, but salaries range to over $100,000 per year for those with permanent positions with established companies in major cities. The same applies to symphony orchestra conductors who, for instance, make $25,000 to $40,000 per year conducting smaller, regional orchestras, but who can make $500,000 or more a year if they become the resident conductor of an internationally famous orchestra.

Conditions of Work

The working conditions of conductors range as widely as their earnings. The conductors of small musical groups at the community level may rehearse in a member's basement, a community center, a high school gym, or in a church or temple. Performances may be held in some of those same places. Lighting, heating or cooling, sound equipment, and musical instrument quality may all be less than adequate. On the other hand, conductors of major orchestras in the larger metropolitan centers usually have ideal working conditions, generally having the same outstanding facilities for rehearsal and performance. Many universities, colleges, and conservatories, even some of the smaller ones, also have state-of-the-art facilities.

Sources of Additional Information

■ **American Federation of Musicians of the United States and Canada**
1501 Broadway, Suite 600
New York, NY 10036
Tel: 212-869-1330

■ **American Guild of Musical Artists**
1727 Broadway
New York, NY 10019
Tel: 212-265-3687

■ **American Symphony Orchestra League**
1156 15th Street, NW, Suite 800
Washington, DC 20005
Tel: 202-776-0212
Email: league@symphony.org

Musical Directors and Conductors

■ **Association of Canadian Orchestras**
56 The Esplanade, Suite 311
Toronto, ON M5E 1A7, Canada
Tel: 416-366-8834
Email: assoc@terraport.net

■ **Conductors' Guild, Inc.**
103 South High Street, Room 6
West Chester, PA 19382
Tel: 215-430-6010

Musicians

School Subjects
Music, Theater/dance

Personal Interests
Entertaining, Music

Work Environment
Indoors and outdoors, Primarily multiple locations

Minimum Education Level
High school diploma

Salary Range
$7,000 to $1,000,000+

Certification or Licensing
Required for certain positions

Outlook
Faster than the average

DOT
152

GOE
01.04.04

NOC
5133

Definition

Musicians perform, compose, conduct, arrange, and teach music. Performers of music would include *singers* as well as *instrumental musicians. Performing musicians* may work alone or as part of a group, or ensemble. They may play before live audiences in clubs or auditoriums, or they may perform on television or radio, in motion pictures, or in a recording studio. Musicians usually play either classical, popular (including country), jazz, or folk music, but many musicians play in several musical styles.

History

According to ancient art and artifacts, humankind has enjoyed music at least since the establishment of early civilizations in the Tigris-Euphrates Valley. Musicians of these early cultures played instruments that were blown, plucked, or struck, just as is done by the musicians of today. Most of the early music, however, was vocal. In the ancient Egyptian temples choirs sang to honor the gods, while in the court musicians accompanied their songs with instruments of the wind, string, and percussion families. The ancient tribes of Israel used a *shofar* (a ram's horn trumpet) to accompany some religious services, a practice that has been continued to the present day. It was the development of music in Greece, however, that clearly influenced Western music. The Greeks had a system of writing their music down, and they invented a system of scales called "modes" that was the forerunner of the modern major and minor scales. Roman music was founded on the Greek model. A seven-tone scale evolved under the Romans, and instrumentation was further developed, including the straight trumpet.

During the Middle Ages, a great catalyst for both change and preservation in music arrived with the development of musical notation, the written language of music. Much credit for this accomplishment is ascribed to Guido d'Arezzo, an eleventh-century Italian monk who devised a system for writing music down on paper, so that it might be preserved and later read and played by other musicians. Many monks during the period devoted their lives to the preservation of the music of the church, and much of the knowledge and development of music is owed to their dedicated efforts. Throughout the Middle Ages, singers and musicians traveled from town to town to play for new audiences. During the Renaissance, singers and musicians often had to depend on wealthy patrons for support. What we now call classical music developed during the Renaissance.

During the seventeenth century, the operatic form developed, most notably in Italy. Opera, combining orchestral music and theater with an extremely popular form of singing, opened up a whole new range of opportunities for musicians, particularly singers. Singers soon began to gain fame in their own right for their incredible vocal feats, and great public demand for their performances allowed them to sever their dependent ties to wealthy patrons.

From about the mid-eighteenth century to the mid-nineteenth century, opportunities for instrumental musicians expanded as composers began to write more complex musical pieces for larger ensembles. During this period, many of the world's great symphonies, concerti, and chamber music were written and performed by musicians playing an ever-widening array of instruments. In the early 1800s came the onset of the Romantic movement in music, in which composers wrote with a new degree of emotionalism and self-expression that conductors and musicians were expected to express in their performance. Around the beginning of the twentieth century musical performers faced another challenge as composers, seeking to break new musical ground, adapted atonal and discordant sounds and new rhythms to their compositions, a direction greatly influenced by the twelve-tone scale of Arnold Schoenberg (1874–1951).

The operatic, classical, and nationalistic music of Europe was brought to America by the migrating Europeans. Throughout the early history of the country, virtually all of the music played was European in style. By the end of the nineteenth century, however, and through the twentieth, musicians came increasingly to play music that was distinctly American in style and composition. At least one musical form, jazz, was entirely an American invention.

The development of popular music and the development of recorded music greatly increased opportunities for musicians. U.S. popular music and jazz influenced music throughout the world. Swing grew out of jazz, and "big" swing bands mushroomed all over the United States during the late 1930s, 1940s, and into the 1950s. Big bands diminished by the late 1950s as rising costs and new popular music styles, such as rhythm and blues and rock and roll, directed the move to smaller groups using electric and electronic instruments. With the advent of electronic mass media, the musical superstar was created, as millions of people at a time could hear and see musical performers. Although the mass electronic media created an enormous market for popular music, it has ironically limited the market for live performances by musicians. The demand for live musicians was also reduced by the widening use of advanced electronic instruments, such as the synthesizer, which itself can replace a whole band, and the DJ (disc jockey), who plays recorded music over highly sophisticated sound systems, replacing musicians at clubs and gatherings.

Until about the mid-1900s, musicians and singers were largely an exploited group who made little money for the use of their skills. The growth of organizations designed to protect performing artists helped greatly to improve the lot of musicians. Particularly effective was the American Federation of Musicians, the musicians' union, which created a wage scale and oversaw the rights of musicians in recording, broadcasting, theater, and at any event in which musicians or their recordings are used. In some situations the union requires that live musicians be hired.

Nature of the Work

Instrumental musicians play one or more musical instruments, usually in a group and in some cases as featured soloists. Musical instruments are usually classified in several distinct categories according to the method by which they produce sound:

strings (violins, cellos, basses, etc.), which make sounds by vibrations from bowing or plucking; woodwinds (oboes, clarinets, saxophones), which make sounds by air vibrations through reeds; brass (trumpets, French horns, trombones, etc.), which make sounds by air vibrations through metal; and percussion (drums, pianos, triangles), which produce sound by striking. Instruments can also be classified as electric or acoustic, especially in popular music. Synthesizers are another common instrument, and computer and other electronic technology is increasingly used for creating music.

Musicians may play in symphony orchestras, dance bands, jazz bands, rock bands, country bands, or other groups or they might go it alone. Some of them may play in recording studios either with their group or as a *session player* for a particular recording. Recordings are in the form of records, tapes, compact discs, and videotape cassettes. Classical musicians perform in concerts, opera performances, and chamber music concerts, and they may also play in theater orchestras, although theater music is not normally classical. The most talented ones may work as soloists with orchestras or alone in recital. Some classical musicians accompany singers and choirs, and they may also perform in churches and temples.

Musicians who play popular music make heavy use of such rhythm instruments as piano, bass, drums, and guitar. Jazz musicians also feature woodwind and brass instruments, especially the saxophone and trumpet, and they extensively utilize the bass. Synthesizers are also commonly used instruments; some music is performed entirely on synthesizers, which can be programmed to imitate a variety of instruments and sounds. Musicians in jazz, blues, country, and rock groups play clubs, festivals, and concert halls and may perform music for recordings, television, and motion picture sound tracks. Occasionally they appear in a movie themselves. Other musicians compose, record, and perform entirely with electronic instruments, such as synthesizers and other devices. In the late 1970s, rap artists began using turntables as musical instruments, and later, samplers, which record a snippet of other songs and sounds, as part of their music.

Instrumental musicians and singers use their skills to convey the form and meaning of written music. Instrumentalists and vocalists work to achieve precision, fluency, and clarity of tone; vocalists attempt to express emotion through phrasing and characterization. Musicians practice constantly to perfect their techniques.

Many musicians supplement their incomes through teaching, while others teach as their full-time occupation, perhaps playing jobs occasionally. Voice and instrumental music teachers work in colleges, high schools, elementary schools, conservatories, and in their own studios; often they give concerts and recitals featuring their students. Many professional musicians give private lessons. Students learn to read music, develop their voices, breathe correctly, and hold their instruments properly.

Choral directors lead groups of singers in schools and other organizations. Church choirs, community oratorio societies, and professional symphony choruses are among the groups that employ choral directors outside of school settings. Choral directors audition singers, select music, and direct singers in achieving the tone, variety, intensity, and phrasing that they feel is required. *Orchestra conductors* do the same with instrumental musicians. Many work in schools and smaller communities, but the best conduct large orchestras in major cities. Some are resident instructors, while others travel constantly, making guest appearances with major national and foreign orchestras. They are responsible for the overall sound and quality of their orchestras.

Musicians may also spend part or all of their time as composers, *arrangers, orchestrators, copyists, librettists,* and *lyricists.* The people in these occupations write and prepare the music that musicians play and sing. Composers write the original music for symphonies, songs, or operas using musical notation to express their ideas through melody, rhythm, and harmony. Arrangers and orchestrators take a composer's work and transcribe it for the various orchestra sections or individual instrumentalists and singers to perform; they prepare music for film scores, musical theater, television, or recordings. Copyists assist composers and arrangers by copying down the various parts of a composition, each of which is played by a different section of the orchestra. Librettists write words to opera and musical theater scores, and lyricists write words to songs and other short musical pieces. A number of songwriters compose both music and lyrics, and many are musicians who perform their own songs.

Requirements

Many musicians begin learning their musical skills at an early age, sometimes before they even enter elementary school. From that point on, the development of musical skills requires long hours of practice and study. Even after high school few students are prepared to take their place as professional musicians; more practice and study are needed. Further institutional study is not required, though, particularly for those seeking a career in the popular music field. College or conservatory degrees would only be required for those who plan to teach in institutions. However, it is probably a good idea for anyone going into music to acquire a degree, just to have a more versatile background in case of a career switch. Some musicians learn to play by ear, but for most, learning musical notation is a requirement.

Scores of colleges and universities have excellent music schools, and there are numerous conservatories that offer degrees in music.

Many schools have noted musicians on their staff, and music students often have the advantage of studying under a professor who has a distinguished career in music. Having the means and a high grade average does not always ensure entry into the top music schools. More than likely an audition is required and only the most talented are accepted. College undergraduates in music school will generally take courses in music theory, harmony, counterpoint, rhythm, melody, ear training, applied music, and music history. Courses in composing, arranging, and conducting are available in most comprehensive music schools. Students will also have to take courses such as English and psychology along with a regular academic program.

Hard work and dedication are key factors in a musical career, but music is an art form, and like those who practice any of the fine arts, musicians will succeed according to the amount of musical talent they have. Those who have talent and are willing to make sacrifices to develop it are the ones most likely to succeed. How much talent and ability one has is always open to speculation and opinion, and it may take years of studying and practice before musicians can assess their own degree of limitation.

There are other requirements necessary to becoming a professional musician that are just as important as training, education, and study. Foremost among these is a love of music strong enough to endure the arduous training and working life of a musician. To become an accomplished musician and to be recognized in the field requires an uncommon degree of dedication, self-discipline, and drive. Musicians who would move ahead must practice constantly with a determination to improve their technique and quality of performance. Musicians also need to develop an emotional toughness that will help them deal with rejection, indifference to their work, and ridicule from critics, which will be especially prevalent early in their careers. There is also praise and adulation along the way, which is easier to take, but also requires a certain psychological handling.

Musicians who want to teach in state elementary and high schools must be state certified. To obtain a state certificate, musicians must satisfactorily complete a degree-granting course in music education at an institution of higher learning. About six hundred institutions in the United States offer programs in music education that qualify students for state certificates. Music education programs include many of the same courses mentioned earlier for musicians in general. They also would include education courses and supervised practice teaching. To teach in colleges and universities or in conservatories generally requires a graduate degree in music. Widely recognized musicians, however, sometimes receive positions in higher education without having obtained a degree.

For musicians interested in careers in popular music, however, little to no formal training is necessary. Many popular musicians teach themselves to play their instruments, which often results in the creation of new and exciting playing styles. Quite often, popular musicians do not even know how to read music. Some would say that many rock musicians do not even know how to play their instrument—this was especially true in the early days of the punk era. Most musicians, however, have a natural talent for rhythm and melody.

Musicians playing popular music, such as rock, jazz, blues, etc., often go through years of "paying their dues"—that is, receiving little money, respect, or attention for their efforts. They must have a strong sense of commitment to their careers and to their creative ideas.

Opportunities for Experience & Exploration

Opportunities for aspiring musicians to explore the field and find early musical experiences are fairly plentiful. Elementary schools, high schools, and institutions of higher education all present students with a number of options for musical training and performance, including choirs, ensembles, bands, and orchestras. Musicians may also have chances to perform in school musicals and talent shows as well. Music students taking private lessons usually are able to display their talents in recitals arranged by their teachers. College, university, and conservatory students also gain valuable performance experience by appearing in recitals and playing in bands, orchestras, and school shows. The more enterprising students in high school and in college form their own bands and begin earning money by playing while still in school.

It is important for aspiring musicians to take advantage of every opportunity to audition as they present themselves. There are numerous community amateur and semiprofessional theater groups throughout the United States that produce musical plays and operettas, in which beginning musicians can gain playing experience. Churches provide numerous opportunities for singers, instrumentalists, and directors to perform and learn. Musical summer camps give young music students a chance to perform with others, gain experience on stage, and begin to find out if they have what it takes to become a professional musician.

Methods of Entering

Young musicians need to enter as many playing situations as they can in their school and community musical groups. They should audition as often as possible, because experience at auditioning is very important. Whenever possible they should take part in seminars and internships offered by orchestras, colleges, and associations. The National Orchestral Association offers training programs for musicians who want a career in the orchestral field.

Musicians who want to perform with established groups, such as choirs and symphony orchestras, enter the field by auditioning. Recommendations from teachers and other musicians often help would-be musicians obtain the opportunity to audition. Concert and opera soloists are also required to audition. Musicians must prepare themselves thoroughly for these auditions, which are demanding and stressful. A bad audition can be very discouraging for the young musician.

Popular musicians often begin playing at low-paying social functions and at small clubs or restaurants. If people like their performances, they usually move on to bookings at larger rooms in better clubs. Continued success leads to a national reputation and possible recording contracts. Jazz musicians tend to operate in the same way, taking every opportunity to audition with established jazz musicians.

Music teachers enter the field by applying directly to schools. College and university placement offices often have listings of positions. Professional associations, in their newsletters and journals also frequently list teaching openings, as do newspapers. An excellent source to check for instrumental jobs is *The International Musician,* the newsletter of The American Federation of Musicians. Other music-oriented journals and associations, such as the American Symphony Orchestra League, can also be contacted for leads and information.

Advancement

Advancement is not easy to define. Popular musicians, once they have become established with a band, advance by moving up to more famous bands or by taking leadership of their own group. Bands may advance from playing small clubs to larger halls and even stadiums and festivals. They may receive a recording contract; if their songs or recordings prove successful, they can command higher fees for their contracts. Symphony orchestra musicians advance by moving to the head of their section of the orchestra. They can also move up to a position such as assistant or associate conductor. Once instrumental musicians acquire a reputation as accomplished artists, they receive engagements that are of higher status and remuneration, and they may come into demand as soloists. As their reputations develop, both classical and popular musicians may receive attractive offers to make recordings and personal appearances.

Popular and opera singers move up to better and more lucrative jobs through recognition of their talent by the public or by music producers and directors and agents. Their advancement is directly related to the demand for their talent and their own ability to promote themselves.

Music teachers in elementary and secondary schools may, with further training, aspire to careers as supervisors of music of a school system, a school district, or an entire state. With further graduate training, teachers can qualify for positions in colleges, universities, and music conservatories, where they can advance to become department heads. Well-known musicians can become artists-in-residence in the music departments of institutions of higher learning.

Employment Outlook

It is difficult to make a living solely as a musician, and this will continue because competition for jobs will be as intense as it has been in the past. Most musicians must hold down other jobs while pursuing their music career. Many thousands of musicians are all trying to "make it" in the music industry. Musicians are advised to be as versatile as possible, playing various kinds of music and more than one instrument. More importantly, they must be committed to pursuing their craft.

A variety of factors will affect musician employment through the year 2005. The demand for musicians will be greatest in theaters, bands, and restaurants as the public continues to spend more money on recreational activities. The outlook is less favorable in churches and temples, though, because of the generally slow growth in religious organizations. The increasing numbers of cable television networks, and increasing numbers of new television programs, will likely see an increase in employment for musicians. The number of record companies has grown dramatically over the last decade, particularly among small, independent houses. Digital recording technology has also made it easier and less expensive for musicians to produce and distribute their own recordings. However, few musicians will earn substantial incomes from these efforts. Popular musicians may receive many short-term engagements in nightclubs, restaurants, and theaters, but these engagements offer little job stability. The supply of musicians for virtually all types of music will continue to exceed the demand for the foreseeable future.

The opportunities for careers in teaching music are expected to grow at an average rate in elementary schools and in colleges and universities but at a slower rate in secondary schools. Although increasing numbers of colleges and universities have begun to offer music programs, enrollments in schools at all levels have been depressed and are not expected to increase until early in the next century. Some public schools, facing severe budget problems, have had to eliminate music programs altogether, making competition for jobs at that level even keener. In addition to these, private music teachers are facing greater competition from instrumental musicians who increasingly must turn to teaching because of the oversupply of musicians seeking playing jobs. The job supply is also diminishing because of the advent of electronic instruments such as synthesizers, which can replace a whole band, and the increasing trend to use recorded music.

Earnings

It is difficult to estimate the earnings of the average musician, because what they can earn is dependent upon the performer's skill, reputation, geographic location, type of music, and number of engagements per year.

Musicians in the major U.S. symphony orchestras earn minimum salaries of between $140 and $1,200 a week. The season for these major orchestras, generally located in the largest U.S. cities, ranges from ten to fifty-two weeks. In major orchestras with annual budgets exceeding $1 million, musicians can earn annual salaries from $18,000 to $60,000 per year. Featured musicians and soloists can earn much more, especially those with an international reputation.

Popular musicians are usually paid per concert or "gig." A band just starting out playing a small bar or club may be required to play three sets a night, and each musician may receive next to nothing for the entire evening. Often, bands receive a percentage of the cover charge at the door. Some musicians play for drinks alone. On average, however, pay per musician ranges from $30 to $300 or more per night. Bands that have gained a recognition and a following may earn far more, because a club owner can usually be assured that many people will come to see the band play. The most successful popular musicians, of course, can earn millions of dollars each year. In the mid-1990s, some artists have signed recording contracts worth $20 million and more.

Musicians are well paid for studio recording work, when they can get it. For recording film and television background music, musicians are paid a minimum of about $185 for a three-hour session; for record company recordings they receive a minimum of about $234 for three hours. Instrumentalists performing live earn anywhere from $30 to

$300 per engagement, depending on their degree of popularity, talent, and the size of the room they play.

Church organists, choir directors, and soloists make an average of $40 to $100 each week, but this is often part-time work supplemented by pay from other jobs.

The salaries received by music teachers in public elementary and secondary schools are the same as for other teachers. In public elementary schools the salary received by teachers in the 1990s is about $24,000 per year. The figure for public secondary school teachers is about $26,100. Music teachers in colleges and universities have widely ranging salaries. Most teachers supplement their incomes through private instruction and by performing in their off hours.

Most musicians do not, as a rule, work steadily for one employer, and they often undergo long periods of unemployment between engagements. Because of these factors, few musicians can qualify for unemployment compensation. Unlike other workers, most musicians also do not enjoy such benefits as sick leave or paid vacations. Some musicians, on the other hand, who work under contractual agreements, do receive benefits, which usually have been negotiated by artists unions, such as the American Federation of Musicians.

Conditions of Work

Work conditions for musicians vary greatly. Performing musicians generally work in the evenings and on weekends. They also spend much time practicing and rehearsing for performances. Their workplace can be almost anywhere, from a swanky club to a high school gymnasium to a dark, dingy bar. Many concerts are given outdoors and in a variety of weather conditions. Performers may be given a star's dressing room or share a mirror in a church basement or find themselves changing in a bar's storeroom. They may work under the hot camera lights of film or television sets or tour with a troupe in subzero temperatures. They may work amid the noise and confusion of a large rehearsal of a Broadway show or in the relative peace and quiet of a small recording studio. Seldom are two days in a performer's life just alike.

Many musicians and singers travel a great deal. More prominent musicians may travel with staffs who make their arrangements and take care of wardrobes and equipment. Their accommodations are usually quite comfortable, if not luxurious, and they are generally playing in major urban centers. Lesser-known musicians may have to take care of all their own arrangements and put up with lesser accommodations in relatively remote places. Some musicians perform on the streets or in subway tunnels and other places likely to have a great deal of passersby. Symphony orchestra musicians probably travel less than most, but those of major orchestras travel largely under first-class conditions.

The chief characteristic of musical employment is its lack of continuity. Few musicians work full-time and most experience periods of unemployment between engagements. Most work day jobs to supplement their incomes. Those who are in great demand generally have agents and managers to help direct their careers.

Music teachers affiliated with institutions work the same hours as other classroom teachers. Many of these teachers, however, spend time after school and on weekends directing and instructing school vocal and instrumental groups. Teachers may also have varied working conditions. They may teach in a large urban school, conducting five different choruses each day, or they may work with rural elementary schools and spend much time driving from school to school.

College or university instructors may divide their time between group and individual instruction. They may teach several musical subjects and may be involved with planning and producing school musical events. They may also supervise student music teachers when they do their practice teaching.

Private music teachers work part- or full-time out of their own homes or in separate studios. The ambiance of their work place would be in accordance with the size and nature of their clientele

Most musicians work in large urban areas and are particularly drawn to the major recording centers, such as Chicago, New York City, Los Angeles, Nashville, and Miami Beach. Most musicians find work in churches, temples, clubs and restaurants, at weddings, in opera and ballet productions, and on television and radio. Religious organizations are the largest single source of work for musicians.

Professional musicians generally hold membership in the American Federation of Musicians (AFL-CIO), and concert soloists also hold membership in the American Guild of Musical Artists, Inc. (AFL-CIO). Singers can belong to a branch of Associated Actors and Artists of America (AFL-CIO). Music teachers in schools often hold membership in the Music Educators National Conference, a department of the National Education Association.

Sources of Additional Information

■ American Federation of Musicians of the United States and Canada
Paramount Building
1501 Broadway, Suite 600
New York, NY 10036
Tel: 212-869-1330

■ **American Guild of Musical Artists**
1727 Broadway
New York, NY 10019
Tel: 212-265-3687

■ **International Guild of Symphony, Opera, and Ballet Musicians**
5802 16th Street, NE
Seattle, WA 98105
Tel: 206-524-7050

■ **Music Teachers National Association**
Carew Tower
441 Vine Street, Suite 505
Cincinnati, OH 45202
Tel: 513-421-1420

■ **National Association of Schools of Music**
11250 Roger Bacon Drive, Suite 21
Reston, VA 20190
Tel: 703-437-0700

■ **Women In Music**
PO Box 441
Radio City Station
New York, NY 10101

Painters and Sculptors

School Subjects
Art, Computer science

Personal Interests
Drawing/painting, Sculpting

Work Environment
Indoors and outdoors, One location with some travel

Minimum Education Level
High school diploma

Salary Range
$30 or less to $300 to $10,000+ per piece, depending on reputation

Certification or Licensing
None

Outlook
About as fast as the average

DOT
144

GOE
01.02.02

Definition

Painters use watercolors, oils, acrylics, and other substances to paint a variety of subjects, including landscapes, people, and objects. *Sculptors* design and construct three-dimensional artwork from various materials, such as stone, concrete, plaster, and wood.

History

Painting and sculpture are probably as old as human civilization. At their essence, painting and sculpture represent attempts to bring order and focus to life and society, and the earliest known artworks were probably created for functional purposes rather than for artistic or aesthetic reasons. For example, the cave paintings of France and Spain, which date from 15,000 BCE, were probably ceremonial in nature, meant to bring good luck to the hunt. From an earlier period, around 21,000 to 25,000 BCE, the Venus of Willendorf, a figure carved from limestone, which along with other figures from the same time might have formed part of fertility rites and rituals and prehistoric relief sculptures, that is, sculptures carved into the walls of caves in France.

Virtually every society has developed its own form of visual expression. At its best, visual art provides a way of viewing culture, tradition, and society, whether those of a civilization that no longer exists or of the modern society in which we live. For most of history, painting and sculpture formed the bases of visual representation. In the late nineteenth century and especially in the twentieth century, new technologies have brought new forms of visual art, such as photography, cinema, video, and computer animation, but their role in society remains about the same: to inform, inspire, provoke, and entertain.

The role of the visual artist in society has developed alongside of the concerns, techniques, and styles of their art. Art, whether painting or sculpture, has ranged from purely decorative to narrative (art that tells a story), from symbolic to realistic. Much of early visual art was religious in nature, reflecting the beliefs and myths with which people tried to understand their place in the world and in life. Art was also used to glorify society or the leaders of society. The immense sculptures of Ramses II (?–1225 BCE) of ancient Egypt, and much of Roman art, served to glorify their rulers and reinforce their stature in society. Often the main subject of a painting or sculpture would appear out of proportion to the other figures in the work, symbolizing their importance or dominance. While this use of artists and their art continues today, the independence we typically associate with modern artists also has its roots in ancient times, as artists sought to create art with more immediately personal concerns.

The art of Greece and Rome exerted a profound influence on much of the history of Western art. The sculptural ideals developed by the ancient Greeks, particularly with their perfection of anatomical forms, continued to dominate Western sculpture until well into the nineteenth century. In painting, artists sought methods to depict or suggest a greater realism, experimenting with techniques of lighting, shading, and others to create an illusion of depth.

The rise of the Christian era brought a return to symbolism over realism. Illuminated manuscripts, which were written texts, usually religious in content, decorated with designs and motifs meant to provide further understanding of the text, became the primary form of artistic expression for nearly a millennium. The artwork for these manuscripts often featured highly elaborate and detailed abstract designs. The human figure was absent in much of this work, reflecting religious prohibition of the creation of idols.

Artists returned to more naturalistic techniques during the fourteenth century with the rise of Gothic art forms. The human figure returned to art; artists began creating art not only for rulers and religious institutions, but also for a growing wealthy class. Portrait painting became an increasingly important source of work and income for artists. New materials, particularly oil glazes and paints, allowed artists to achieve more exact detailing and more subtle light, color, and shading effects.

During the Renaissance, artists rediscovered the art of ancient Greece and Rome. This brought new developments not only in artists' techniques, but also in their stature in society. The development of perspective techniques in the fourteenth and fifteenth centuries revolutionized painting. Perspective allowed the artists to create the illusion of three dimensions, so that a spectator felt that he or she looked not merely at a painting, but into it. Advances in the study of anatomy enabled artists to create more dramatic and realistic figures, whether in painting or sculpture, providing the illusion of action and fluidity and heightening the naturalism of their work. The role of the artist changed from simple artisan or craftsman to creative force. They were sought out by the wealthy, the church, and rulers for their talent and skill, receiving commissions for new work or being supported by patrons as they worked.

The work of Giotto (1266–1337), Michelangelo (1475–1564), Raphael (1483–1520), Leonardo da Vinci (1452–1519), Titian (1477–1576), and other Renaissance artists continue to fascinate people today. Artists developed new concerns for the use of line, color, contour, shading, setting, and composition, presenting work of greater realism and at the same time of deeper emotional content. The style of an artist became more highly individualized, more a personal reflection of the artist's thoughts, beliefs, ideas, and feelings. The fantastic, nightmare-like paintings of Hieronymus Bosch (1450?–1516) opened new areas of thematic and subjective exploration. In the late Renaissance, new styles began to emerge, such as the mannerist style of El Greco (1541?–1614?) of Spain and the northern styles of Albrecht Durer (1471–1528) and Pieter Bruegel the Elder (1525?–69), and the subject matter of painting was extended to depict common scenes of ordinary life.

Artists continued to influence one other, but national and cultural differences began to appear in art as the Catholic church lost its dominance and new religious movements took hold. Art academies, such as the Academie Royale de Peinture et de Sculture in Paris, were established and sought to codify artistic ideals. The works of the Flemish painter Peter Paul Rubens (1577–1640), the Dutch painters Vermeer (1632–75) and Rembrandt (1606–69), and the French painter Nicolas Poussin (1594–1665) highlight the different techniques, styles, and concerns rising during the baroque period of the seventeenth century.

The next two centuries would see profound changes in the nature of art, leading to the revolutionary work of the impressionists of the late nineteenth century and the dawn of the modern era in art. Sculpture, which had remained largely confined to the Greek and Roman ideals, found new directions beginning with the work of Rodin (1840–1917). The individual sensibility of the artist himself took on a greater importance and led to a greater freedom of painting techniques, such as in the work of John Constable (1776–1837) and J.M.W. Turner (1775–1851) of England. In France, Gustave Courbet (1819–77) challenged many of the ideals of the French academy, leading to the avant-garde work of the early French impressionists. Artists began to take on a new role by challenging society with new concepts, ideas, and visions, and radical departures in style. Artists no longer simply reflected prevailing culture, but adopted leadership positions in creating culture, often rejecting entirely the artistic principles of the past. The revolutionary works of Edouard Manet (1832–83), Edgar Degas (1834–1917), Claude Monet (1840–1926), Georges Seurat (1859–91), Paul Cezanne (1839–1906), and others would in turn be rejected by succeeding generations of artists intent on developing new ideas and techniques. The image of the artist as cultural outsider or societal misfit or even tormented soul took hold, with painters such as Paul Gauguin (1848–1903), Edvard Munch (1863–1944), and Vincent Van Gogh (1853–90). Artists working in the avant garde achieved notoriety, if not financial reward, and the "misunderstood" or "starving" artist became a popular twentieth century image.

The twentieth century witnessed an explosion of artistic styles and techniques. Art, both in painting and sculpture, became increasingly abstracted from reality, and purely formal concerns developed. Impressionism and postimpressionism gave way to futurism, expressionism, Henri Matisse's (1869–1954) fauvism, the cubism developed by Pablo Picasso (1881–73) and Georges Braque (1882–1963), the nonobjective paintings of Wassily Kandinsky (1866–1944), Piet Mondrian (1874–1944) and Salvadore Dali's (1904–89) surrealism, and others.

American art, which had largely followed the examples set by European artists, came into its own during the 1940s and 1950s, with the rise of abstract expressionism lead by Willem de Kooning (born 1904) and Jackson Pollock (1912–56). During the 1950s, a new art form, pop art, reintroduced recognizable images. The work of Richard Hamilton, Andy Warhol (1927–87), Roy Lichtenstein (born 1923), and others used often mundane objects, such as Warhol's Campbell soup cans, to satirize and otherwise comment on cultural and societal life.

More recent trends in art have given the world the graffiti-inspired works of Keith Haring and the "non-art" sculpture of Jeff Koons, as well as the massive installations of Christo. Artists today work in a great variety of styles, forms, and media. Many artists combine elements of painting, sculpture, and other art forms, such as photography, music, and dance, into their work. The rise of video recording techniques, and especially of three-dimensional computer animations has recently begun to challenge many traditional ideas of art.

Nature
of the Work

Painters and sculptors use their creative abilities to produce original works of art. They are generally classified as fine artists rather than commercial artists because they are responsible for selecting the theme, subject matter, and medium of their artwork. As fine artists, painters and sculptors create works to be viewed and judged for aesthetic content. Visual art can take as many forms as the people who create them.

Painters use a variety of media to paint portraits, landscapes, still lifes, abstracts, and other subjects. They use brushes, palette knives, and other artist's tools to apply color to canvas or other surfaces. They work in a variety of media, including oil paint, acrylic paint, tempora, watercolors, pen and ink, pencil, charcoal, crayon, pastels, but may also use such nontraditional media as earth, clay, cement, paper, cloth, and any other material that allows them to express their artistic ideas. Painters develop line, space, color, and other visual elements to produce the desired effect. They may prefer a particular style of art, such as realism or abstract, and they may be identified with a certain technique or subject matter. Many artists develop a particular style and apply that style across a broad range of techniques, from painting to etching to sculpture.

Sculptors use a combination of media and methods to create three-dimensional works of art. They may carve objects from stone, plaster, concrete, or wood. They may use their fingers to model clay or wax into objects. Some sculptors create forms from metal or stone, using various masonry tools and equipment. Others create works from found objects, whether parts of a car, branches of a tree, or other objects. Like painters, sculptors may be identified with a particular technique or style. Their work can take monumental forms or they may work on a very small scale.

Many artists, of course, combine both elements of painting and sculpture in their art. They may also combine techniques of music, dance, photography, and even science, engineering, mechanics, and electronics in their work.

Sculptors creating large works, especially those that will be placed outdoors and in public areas, usually work under contract or commission. Most artists, however, create works that express their personal artistic vision and then hope to find someone to purchase them. Artists generally seek out a gallery to display their work and function as the sales agent for the work. The gallery owner and artist set the prices for pieces of art, and the gallery owner receives a commission on any work that sells. The relationship between the gallery owner and artist is often one of close cooperation, and the gallery owner may encourage the artist to explore new techniques, styles, and ideas, while helping to establish a reputation for the artist. As an artist becomes well known, selling his or her work often becomes easier, and many well-known artists receive commissions for their art.

There is no single way to become or to be an artist. As with other areas of the arts, painting and sculpting usually are intensely personal endeavors. If it is possible to generalize, most painters and sculptors are people with a desire and need to explore visual representations of the world around them or the world within them, or both. Throughout their careers, they seek to develop their vision and the methods and techniques that allow them to best express themselves. Many artists work from or within a tradition or style of art. They may develop formal theories of art or advance new theories of visual presentation. Painters and sculptors are usually aware of the art that has come before them as well as the work of their contemporaries.

Every painter and sculptor has his or her own way of working. Many work in studios, often separate from their homes, where they can produce their work in privacy and quiet. Many artists, however, work outdoors. Most artists probably combine both indoor and outdoor work during their careers. An artist may choose complete solitude in order to work; others thrive on interaction with other artists and people. Artists engaged in monumental work, particularly sculptors, often have people who assist in the creation of a piece of art, working under the artist's direction. They may contract with a foundry in order to cast the finished sculpture in bronze, iron, or another metal. As film, video, and computer technology has developed, the work of painters and sculptors has expanded into new forms of expression. The recently developed three-dimensional computer animation techniques in particular often blur the boundaries between painting, sculpture, photography, and cinema.

The work of an artist usually continues throughout his or her lifetime. Creating fine art is rarely a career choice but rather a way of life, a following of a desire or need that may exhibit itself at an extremely early age. Visual artists use their work to communicate what they see, feel, think, believe, or simply are in a form other than language. For some artists, this may be the only way they feel they can truly communicate.

Requirements

There are no educational requirements for becoming a painter or sculptor. However, most artists benefit from training, and many attend art schools or programs in colleges and universities. There are also many workshops and other ways for artists to gain instruction, practice, and exposure to art and the works and ideas of other artists. The artist should learn a variety of techniques, be exposed to as many media and styles as possible, and gain an understanding of the history of art and art theory. By learning as much as possible, the artist is better able to choose the appropriate means for his or her own artistic expression.

An important requirement for a career as a painter or sculptor is artistic ability. Of course, this is entirely subjective, and it is perhaps more important that artists believe in their own ability, or in their own potential. Apart from being creative and imaginative, painters and sculptors should exhibit such traits as patience, persistence, determination, independence, and sensitivity.

Because earning a living as a fine artist is very difficult, especially when one is just starting out, many painters and sculptors work at another job. With the proper training and educational background, many painters and sculptors are able to work in art-related positions as art teachers, art directors, or graphic designers, while pursuing their own art activities independently. For example, many art teachers hold classes in their own studios.

Both painters and sculptors should be good at business and sales if they intend to support themselves through their art. As small-business people, they must be able to market and sell their products to wholesalers, retailers, and the general public.

Artists who sell their works to the public may need special permits from the local or state tax office. In addition, artists should check with the Internal Revenue Service for laws on selling and tax information related to income received from the sale of artwork.

Many artists join professional organizations that provide informative advice and tips as well as opportunities to meet with other artists.

Opportunities for Experience & Exploration

Experience in drawing, painting, and even sculpting can be had at a very early age, even before formal schooling begins. Most elementary, middle, and high schools offer classes in art. Aspiring painters and sculptors can undertake a variety of artistic projects at school or at home. Many arts associations and schools also offer beginning classes in various types of art for the general public.

Students interested in pursuing art as a career are encouraged to visits museums and galleries to view the work of other artists. In addition, they can learn about the history of art and artistic techniques and methods through books, videotapes, and other sources.The New York Foundation for the Arts sponsors a toll-free hotline, 800-232-2789, which offers quick information on programs and services and answers to specific questions on visual artists. The hotline is open Monday through Friday, between 2 and 5 PM Eastern Standard Time.

Methods of Entering

Artists interested in exhibiting or selling their products should investigate potential markets. Reference books, such as *Artist's Market,* may be helpful, as well as library books that offer information on business laws, taxes, and related issues. Local fairs and art shows often provide opportunities for new artists to display their work. Art councils are a good source of information on upcoming fairs in the area.

Some artists sell their work on consignment. When a painter or sculptor sells work this way, a store or gallery displays an item; when the item is sold, the artist gets the price of that item minus a commission that goes to the store or gallery. Artists who sell on consignment should read contracts very carefully.

Many art schools and universities have placement services to help students find jobs. Although fine artists are generally self-employed, many need to work at another job, at least initially, to support themselves while they establish a reputation.

Advancement

Painters and sculptors are self-employed; thus, the channels for advancement are not as well defined as they are at a company or firm. An artist may become increasingly well known, both nationally and internationally, and as an artist's reputation increases, he or she can command higher prices for his or her work. The success of the fine artist depends on a variety of factors, including talent, drive, and determination. However, luck often seems to play a role in many artists' success, and some artists do not achieve recognition until late in life, if at all. Artists with business skills may open their own galleries to display their own and others' work. Those with the appropriate educational backgrounds may become art teachers, agents, or critics.

Employment Outlook

The employment outlook for painters and sculptors is difficult to predict. Because they are usually self-employed, much of their success depends on the amount and type of work created, the drive and determination in selling the artwork, and the interest or readiness of the public to appreciate and purchase the work.

Success for an artist, however, is difficult to quantify. Individual artists may consider themselves successful as their talent matures and they are better able to present their vision in their work. This type of success goes beyond financial considerations. Few artists enter this field for the money. Financial success depends on a great deal of factors, many of which have nothing to do with the artist or his or her work. Artists with good marketing skills will likely be the most successful in selling their work. Although artists should not let their style be dictated by market trends, those interested in financial success can attempt to determine what types of artwork are wanted by the public.

It often takes several years for an artist's work and reputation to be established. Many artists have to support themselves through other employment. There are numerous employment opportunities for commercial artists in such fields as publishing, advertising, fashion and design, and teaching. Painters and sculptors should consider employment in these and other fields. They should be prepared, however, to face strong competition from others who are attracted to these fields.

Earnings

The amount of money earned by painters and sculptors varies greatly. Most are self-employed and set their own hours and prices. Artists often work long hours and earn little, especially when they are first starting out. The price they charge is up to them, but much depends on the value the public places on their work. A particular item may sell for a few dollars, a few hundred, or a few thousand or tens of thousands of dollars and more. Often, the value of an artwork may increase considerably after it has been sold. An artwork that may have earned an artist only a few hundred dollars may earn many thousands of dollars the next time it is sold.

Some artists obtain grants that allow them to pursue their art; others win prizes and awards in competitions. Most artists, however, have to work on their projects part-time while holding down a regular, full-time job. Many artists teach in art schools, high schools, or out of their studios. Artists who sell their products must pay social security and other taxes on any money they receive.

Conditions of Work

Most painters and sculptors work out of their homes or in studios. Some work in small areas in their apartments; others work in large, well-ventilated lofts. Occasionally, painters and sculptors work outside. In addition, artists often work at fairs, shops, museums, and other places where their work is being exhibited.

Artists often work long hours, and those who are self-employed do not receive paid vacations, insurance coverage, or any of the other benefits usually offered by a company or firm. However, artists are able to work at their own pace, set their own prices, and make their own decisions. The energy and creativity that go into an artist's work brings feelings of pride and satisfaction. Most artists genuinely love what they do.

Sources of Additional Information

■ **American Society of Artists**
PO Box 1326
Palatine, IL 60078

■ **National Art Education Association**
1916 Association Drive
Reston, VA 22091-1590
Tel: 703-860-8000
Email: naea@dgs.dgsys.com

■ **National Endowment for the Arts**
Nancy Hanks Center
Arts and Education
Education and Access Division
1100 Pennsylvania Avenue, NW
Washington, DC 20506-0001
Tel: 202-682-5426

■ **Sculptors Guild**
The Soho Building
110 Greene Street
New York, NY 10012
Tel: 212-431-5669

Photographers

School Subjects
Art, Business

Personal Interests
Drawing/painting, Photography

Work Environment
Indoors and outdoors, Primarily multiple locations

Minimum Education Level
Some postsecondary training

Salary Range
$16,500 to $38,900+

Certification or Licensing
Recommended

Outlook
Faster than the average

DOT
143

GOE
01.02.02

NOC
5221

Definition

Photographers take and sometimes develop pictures of people, places, objects, and events, using a variety of cameras and photographic equipment. The work may be ordered by individuals who want photographic records or keepsakes or by companies that use commercial photographers for various business purposes.

History

The word *photograph* means, literally, "to write with light." Although the art of photography goes back only about 150 years, the two Greek words that were chosen and combined to refer to this skill quite accurately describe what it does.

The discoveries that led eventually to photography began early in the eighteenth century when a German scientist, Dr. Johann H. Schultze, experimented with the action of light on certain chemicals. He found that when these chemicals were covered by dark paper they did not change color, but when they were exposed to sunlight, they darkened. This observation led eventually to the work of a French painter named Louis Daguerre (1787–1851), who became the first photographer in 1839, when he perfected the process of using silver-iodide-coated plates inside a small box. He then developed the plates by means of mercury vapor. The daguerreotype, as these early photographs came to be known, took minutes to expose and the developing process was directly to the plate. There were no prints made.

Although the daguerreotype was the sensation of its day, it was not until George Eastman (1854–1932) invented a simple camera and flexible roll film that photography began to come into widespread use in the late 1800s. With exposure to the negative, light-sensitive paper was used to make positive multiple copies of the image.

Nature of the Work

Photography is both an artistic and technical occupation because many still photographers produce pictures that not only reveal their own proficiency but are so beautifully composed that they are works of fine art. In all kinds of photographic work, the photographer must be able to use a variety of cameras, lenses, and filters to achieve a desired effect. They must know many kinds of film and know which to use for different types of pictures, lighting conditions, cameras, and filters. They also need to know and be able to use a variety of types of lighting equipment. In addition, photographers must be familiar with film processing techniques that develop, enlarge, and print photographs. In many large studios, photographic technicians are employed to process film and technical reproduction while in smaller shops photographers may have to do it themselves.

Many professional still photographers specialize in areas such as portrait work, commercial photography, and industrial photography. *Portrait photographers* take photos of individuals, couples, or small groups. They try to attain not only a natural-looking and attractive effect but also one that expresses the personality of the individuals. Most portrait photographers work in their own studios, although they may go to people's homes and other locations to take photographs.

Commercial photographers usually take photos of consumer and industrial products, such as machinery, fashions, and retail merchandise, and building exteriors and interiors, to be used in advertising and marketing. A great variety of cameras, lights, and props are used in commercial photography, and the photographer must have a full command of all kinds of photographic techniques.

The *industrial photographer* does work that is similar to that of the commercial photographer. The main emphasis, however, is on taking pictures for a single company or firm that may lead to the improvement of factory organization and products. To accomplish this end, the industrial photographer takes pictures of workers on the job and of equipment and machinery operating at high speed. The pictures are generally used in company publications or for advertising company products or services.

Other photographic specialists include the following:

Photojournalists take pictures of newsworthy events, people, places, and things for newspapers and magazines, combining an ability to find and record dramatic action with photographic talent. Some photojournalists specialize in educational photography and prepare slides, film strips, videos, and motion pictures for use in classrooms and training programs.

Aerial photographers take photographs from aircraft in flight for news, business, industrial, scientific, weather, or military purposes.

Scientific photographers and *biological photographers* provide photographic illustrations and documentation for scientific publications and research reports. They usually specialize in a field such as engineering, aerodynamics, medicine, biology, or chemistry.

Finish photographers photograph the results of horse races as the horses approach and cross the finish line.

Nightclub and restaurant photographers circulate among guests and take photographs of customers who request them.

Some photographers write for trade and technical journals, teach photography in schools and colleges, act as representatives of photographic equipment manufacturers, sell photographic equipment and supplies, produce documentary films, or do freelance work.

Requirements

Formal educational requirements depend upon the nature of the photographer's specialty. For instance, photographic work in scientific and engineering research generally requires an engineering background with a degree from a recognized college or institute.

A college education is not required to become a photographer, although college training probably offers the most promising assurance of success in fields such as industrial, news, or scientific photography. In the 1990s, 103 community and junior colleges offer associate degrees in photography, more than 160 colleges and universities offer bachelor's degrees, and 38 offer master's degrees. Many of these schools offer courses in cinematography, although very few have programs leading to a degree in this specialty. Many men and women, however, become photographers with no formal education beyond high school.

Prospective photographers should have a broad technical understanding of photography plus as much practical experience with cameras as possible. They should take many different kinds of photographs with a variety of cameras and subjects. They should learn how to develop photographs and, if possible, should have a darkroom. Experience in picture composition, cropping prints (cutting to desired size), enlarging, and retouching are all valuable.

Students who hope to become photographers should possess manual dexterity, good eyesight and color vision, and artistic ability. They should have an eye for form and line, an appreciation of light and shadow, and the ability to use imaginative and creative approaches to photographs or film, especially in commercial work. In addition, they should be patient and accurate and enjoy working with detail.

Self-employed, or freelance, photographers need good business skills. They must be able to manage their own studios, including hiring and managing photographic assistants and other employees, keeping records, and maintaining photographic and business files. Marketing and sales skills are also important to a successful freelance photography business.

Opportunities for Experience & Exploration

Photography is a field that almost every person with a camera can explore. Students can join high school camera clubs, yearbook of newspaper staffs, photography contests, and community hobby groups to gain experience. Students also may seek a part-time or summer job in a camera shop or work as a developer in a laboratory or processing center.

Methods of Entering

There is no one way in which to become a photographer. Some people enter the field as apprentices, trainees, or assistants. A trainee may work in a darkroom, camera shop, or developing laboratory. Trainees may move lights and arrange backgrounds for a commercial or portrait photographer or motion picture photographer. They may spend many months learning this kind of work before they move into a job behind a camera. In many large cities, there are schools of photography, which may be a good way to start in the field. A *press photographer* may work for one of the many newspapers and magazines published in the United States and abroad. Some employers require a probationary period of thirty to ninety days before a new employee attains full job security. On publications where there is a full Newspaper Guild shop, a photographer will be required to join the guild.

Some go into business for themselves as soon as they have finished their formal education. Setting up a studio may not require a large capital outlay, but beginners may find that success does not come easily.

Advancement

Because photography is such a diversified field, there is no usual way in which to get ahead. Those who begin by working for someone else may advance to owning their own businesses. Commercial photographers may gain prestige as more of their pictures are placed in well-known trade journals or popular magazines. Press photographers may advance in salary and the kinds of important news stories assigned to them. A few photographers may become celebrities in their own right by making contributions to medical science, engineering science, or natural or physical science.

Employment Outlook

About 90,000 photographers are employed in the 1990s. About half are salaried employees; the rest are self-employed. Most jobs for photographers are provided by photographic or commercial art studios; other employers include newspapers and magazines, radio and TV broadcasting, government agencies, and manufacturing firms. Colleges, universities, and other educational institutions employ photographers to prepare promotional and educational materials.

There will be a very favorable employment increase in photography throughout the 1990s as the use of visual images continues to grow in areas such as communications, education, entertainment, marketing, and research and development. In business and industry, for example, greater use will be made of photographs in meetings, stockholders' reports, annual reports, sales campaigns, and public relations programs. Excellent opportunities should exist for scientific and medical photographers. Photojournalism is expected to show slow growth.

Earnings

The earnings of photographers in private industry vary according to the level of responsibility. In the 1990s, those who handle routine work earn an average of about $24,800 a year. Photographers who do difficult or challenging work earn approximately $37,200 a year.

In the 1990s, beginning photographers working for newspapers that had contracts with the Newspaper Guild earn a median salary of about $19,000 a year. Most earn between $16,500 and $22,500, with the top ten percent receiving $26,500 or more. Experienced newspaper photographers earn a median of $30,700 a year; most earn from $26,300 to $35,700 a year. The top ten percent of experienced newspaper photographers earn in excess of $38,900.

Photographers in government service earn an average salary of about $29,500 a year. Self-employed photographers often earn more than salaried photographers, but their earnings depend on general business conditions. In addition, self-employed photographers do not have the benefits that a company provides its employees.

Photographers who combine scientific training and photographic expertise, as do scientific photographers, usually start at higher salaries than other photographers. They also usually receive consistently larger advances in salary than do others, so that their income, both as beginners and as experienced photographers, place them well above the average in their field. Photographers in salaried jobs usually receive benefits such as paid holidays, vacations, and sick leave and medical insurance.

Conditions of Work

Work conditions vary based on the job and employer. Many photographers work a thirty-five to forty-hour workweek, but freelancers and news photographers often put in long, irregular hours. Commercial and portrait photographers work in comfortable surroundings. Photojournalists seldom are assured physical comfort in their work and may in fact face danger when covering stories on natural disasters or military conflicts. Some photographers work in research laboratory settings; others work on aircraft; and still others work underwater. For some photographers, conditions change from day to day. One day, they may be photographing a hot and dusty rodeo; the next they may be taking pictures of a dog sled race in Alaska.

In general, photographers work under pressure to meet deadlines and satisfy customers. Freelance photographers have the added pressure of continually seeking new clients and uncertain incomes.

For specialists in fields such as fashion photography, breaking into the field may take years. Working as another photographer's assistant is physically demanding when carrying equipment is required.

For freelance photographers, the cost of equipment can be quite expensive, with no assurance that the money spent will be recouped through income from future assignments. Freelancers in travel-related photography, such as travel and tourism, and photojournalism have the added cost of transportation and accommodations. For all photographers, flexibility is a major asset.

Sources of Additional Information

■ **American Society of Media Photographers**
419 Park Avenue, South
New York, NY 10016
Tel: 609-799-8300

■ **Newspaper Guild**
Education Department
8611 Second Avenue
Silver Spring, MD 20910
Tel: 301-585-2990

■ **Professional Photographers of America**
57 Forsyth Street, NW, Suite 1600
Atlanta, GA 30303
Tel: 404-522-8600

Producers

School Subjects
Business, English (writing/literature)

Personal Interests
Film and Television

Work Environment
Primarily indoors, Primarily one location

Minimum Education Level
High school diploma

Salary Range
$15,000 to $200,000+

Certification or Licensing
None

Outlook
About as fast as the average

DOT
187

GOE
01.03.01

NOC
5121

Definition

Producers organize and secure the financial backing for the production of motion pictures. They decide which scripts will be used or which books will be adapted for film. Producers also raise money to finance the filming of a motion picture; hire the director, screenwriter, and cast; oversee the budget and production schedule; and monitor the distribution of the film.

Many in the field are self-employed, or independent, producers. Others are salaried employees of film companies, television networks, and television stations.

History

Motion picture cameras were invented in the late 1800s. The two earliest known films-made in 1888 by French-born Louis Le Prince-showed his father-in-law's garden and traffic crossing an English bridge.

More advanced cameras and motion picture techniques quickly followed. In 1903 American director Edwin Porter and inventor Thomas Edison (1847–1931) made *The Great Train Robbery,* one of the first movies in which scenes were filmed out of sequence; when the filming was completed, the scenes were edited and spliced together. By 1906 feature-length films were being made and many talented and financially savvy individuals were making their livings as producers. The first woman to become a producer was Alice Guy, who started the Solax Company in New York in 1910.

In 1911 the Centaur Company, which had been trying to film westerns in New Jersey, moved to California and became the first studio to settle in Hollywood. Many film companies followed the lead of Centaur and moved their operations to southern California where there was abundant sunshine and a variety of terrain.

The film industry began to consolidate in the late 1920s after the introduction of sound films and the 1929 stock market crash. Small and marginally profitable producers were forced out of business, leaving the largest companies, which controlled most of the first-run theaters, to dominate the market. Major studios produced their films in a factory-like fashion. With their permanent staff of cameramen and other technical workers, a major studio could produce forty or more films annually. And because many of the larger studios also owned their own network of theaters throughout the United States, they had a guaranteed market to which they could distribute their films. This stable, mass-produced system gave some studios the encouragement to produce commercially risky art films as well.

The introduction of television after World War II brought mixed fortunes to motion picture producers. Television was partly responsible for a decline in the number of theatergoers, causing financial difficulties for the studios. An antitrust court judgment against the studios also eliminated their dominance of the movie theater market. But with the emergence and growth of television, and a steady need for new shows and made-for-TV films, television broadened employment opportunities for producers.

The major studios experienced financial difficulties in the 1950s, which because of studio downsizing and other pressures, led to a growth in the number of independent producers. Changes in the U.S. tax code made independent producing even more profitable. In response to their financial difficulties, studios began to reduce the number of films produced each year and to rely more on expensive "blockbuster" films to attract audiences.

In the early 1970s the industry again went through a major reorganization. The staggering expense of producing blockbusters had drained the major studios of their profits, and these financially strapped companies began to make films under strict cost-containment measures. Film projects, moreover, were increasingly initiated by independent producers.

Technical innovations have had great influence on motion picture producing. Portable lights, cameras, and other equipment allow films to be made anywhere and reduce the dependence on studio sets. More recently, the emergence of cable television and the ensuing demand for new shows has opened a new market for film producers. In recent years, the traditional distinctions between television and movie production, as well as between American and foreign films, have become increasingly blurred. Many foreign-made films are now financed by Americans, and a number of American motion picture companies have foreign owners.

Nature of the Work

The primary role of a producer is to organize and secure the financial backing necessary to undertake a motion picture project. The director, by contrast, creates the film from the screenplay. Despite this general distinction, the producer often takes part in creative decisions, and occasionally one person is both the producer and director. On some small projects, such as a nature or historical documentary for a public television broadcast, the producer might also be the writer and cameraman.

The job of a producer generally begins in the preproduction stage of filmmaking with the selection of a movie idea from a script, or other material. Some films are made from original screenplays, while others are adapted from books. If a book is selected, the producer must first purchase the rights from the author or his or her publishing company, and a writer must be hired to adapt the book into a screenplay format. Producers are usually inundated with scripts from writers and others who have ideas for a movie. Producers may have their own idea for a motion picture and will hire a writer to write the screenplay. Occasionally a studio will approach a producer, typically a producer who has had many commercially or artistically successful films in the past, with a project.

After selecting a project, the producer will find a director, the technical staff, and the star actor or actors to participate in the film. Along with the script and screenwriter, these essential people are referred to as the "package." Packaging is sometimes arranged with the help of talent agencies. It is the package that the producer tries to sell to an investor to obtain the necessary funds to finance the salaries and cost of the film.

There are three common sources for financing a film: major studios, production companies, and individual investors. A small number of producers have enough money to pay for their own projects. Major studios are the largest source of money and finance most of the big budget films. Although some studios have full-time producers on staff, they hire independent producers for many projects. Large production companies often have the capital resources to fund projects which they feel will be commercially successful. On the smaller end of the scale, producers of documentary films commonly approach individual donors; foundations; art agencies of federal, state, and local governments; and even family members and churches. The National Endowment for the Humanities and the National Endowment for the Arts are major federal benefactors of cinema.

Raising money from individual investors can occupy much of the producer's time. Fund-raising may be done on the telephone, as well as in conferences, business lunches, and even cocktail parties. The producer may also look for a distributor for the film even before the production begins.

Obtaining the necessary financing does not guarantee a film will be made. After raising the money, the producer takes the basic plan of the package and tries to work it into a developed project. The script may be rewritten several times, the full cast of actors is hired, salaries are negotiated, and logistical problems, such as the location of the filming, are worked out. On some projects it might be the director who handles these tasks, or the director may work with the producer. Most major motion film projects do not get beyond this complicated stage of development.

During the production phase, the producer tries to keep the project on schedule and spending within the established budget. Other production tasks include the review of dailies, which are prints of the day's filming. As the head of the project, the producer is ultimately responsible for resolving all problems, including personal conflicts such as those between the director and an actor and the director and the studio. If the film is successfully completed, the producer monitors its distribution and may participate in the publicity and advertising of the film.

To accomplish the many and varied tasks that the position requires, producers hire a number of subordinates, such as associate producers, sometimes called *coproducers*, line producers, and production assistants. Job titles, however, vary from project to project. In general, *associate producers* work directly under the producer and oversee the major areas of the project, such as the budget. *Line producers* handle the day-to-day operations of the project. *Production assistants* may perform substantive tasks, such as reviewing scripts, but others are hired to be errand-runners. Another position, *executive producer,* often refers to the person who puts up the money, such as a studio executive, though it is sometimes an honorary title with no functional relevance to the project.

Requirements

There is no minimum educational requirement for becoming a producer. Many producers, however, are college graduates, and many also have a business degree or other previous business experience. They must not only be talented salespeople and administrators but must also have a thorough understanding of films and motion picture technology. Such understanding, of course, only comes from experience.

Formal study of film, television, communications, theater, writing, English literature, or art are helpful, as the producer must have the background to know whether an idea or script is worth pursuing. Many entry-level positions in the film industry are given to people who have studied liberal arts, cinema, or both. In the United States there are more than a thousand colleges, universities, and trade schools that offer classes in film or television studies; more than 120 of these offer undergraduate programs, and more than fifty grant master's degrees. A small number of Ph.D. programs also exist.

Graduation from a film or television program does not guarantee employment in the industry. Some programs are quite expensive, costing more than $50,000 in tuition alone for three years of study. Others do not have the resources to allow all students to make their own films. Programs in Los Angeles and New York, the major centers of the entertainment industry, may provide the best opportunities for making contacts that can be of benefit when seeking employment.

Producers come from a wide variety of backgrounds. Some start out as magazine editors, business school graduates, actors, or secretaries, messengers, and production assistants for a film studio. Many have never formally studied film. Most producers, however, get their position through several years of experience in the industry, perseverance, and a keen sense for what projects will be artistically and commercially successful.

Opportunities for Experience & Exploration

There are many ways to gain experience in filmmaking. Some high schools have film and video clubs, for example, or courses on the use of motion picture equipment. Experience in high school or college theater can also be useful. One of the best ways to get experience is to volunteer for a student or low-budget film project; positions on such projects are often advertised in local trade publications. Community cable stations also hire volunteers and may even offer internships.

Methods of Entering

Becoming a producer is similar to becoming president of a company. Unless a person is independently wealthy and can finance whichever projects he or she chooses, prior experience in the field is necessary. Because there are so few positions, even with experience it is extremely difficult to become a successful producer.

Most motion picture producers have attained their position only after years of moving up the industry ladder. Thus, it is important to concentrate on immediate goals, such as getting an entry-level position in a film company. Some enter the field by getting a job as a production assistant. An entry-level production assistant may photocopy copies of the scripts for the actors to use, assist in setting up equipment, or may perform other menial tasks, often for very little or even no pay. While a production assistant's work is often tedious and seemingly of little reward, it nevertheless does expose one to the intricacies of filmmaking and, more importantly, creates an opportunity to make contacts with others in the industry.

Those interested in the field should approach film companies, television stations, or the television networks about employment opportunities as a production assistant. Small television stations often provide the best opportunity for those who are interested in television producing. Positions may also be listed in trade publications.

Advancement

There is little room for advancement beyond the position, as producers are at the top of their profession. Advancement for producers is generally measured by the types of projects, increased earnings, and respect in the field. At television stations, a producer can advance to program director. Some producers become directors or make enough money to finance their own projects.

Employment Outlook

In the 1990s the greatest concentration of motion picture producers is in Hollywood and New York. Hollywood alone has more than two thousand producers.

The employment outlook for producers is expected to remain extremely competitive throughout the 1990s and into the twenty-first century. Opportunities might increase with the expansion of cable television and an increased overseas demand for American-made films.

Earnings

Producers are generally paid a percentage of the project's profits, or according to a fee negotiated between the producer and a studio. Average yearly earnings range from about $25,000 to $70,000. Producers of highly successful films can earn as much as $200,000 or more, while those who make low-budget, documentary films might earn considerably less than average. In general, producers in the film industry earn more than those in television. Entry-level production assistants can earn from less than minimum wage to $15,000 per year.

Conditions of Work

Producers have greater control over their working conditions than most other people working in the motion picture industry. They may have the autonomy of choosing their own projects, setting their own hours, and delegating duties to others as necessary. The work often brings considerable personal satisfaction. But it is not without constraints. Producers must work within a stressful schedule complicated by competing work pressures and often daily crises. Each project brings a significant financial and professional risk. Long hours and weekend work are common. Most producers must provide for their own health insurance and other benefits.

Sources of Additional Information

■ **Producers Guild of America**
400 South Beverly Drive
Beverly Hills, CA 90212
Tel: 310-557-0807

Production Assistants

School Subjects
Business, Theater/dance

Personal Interests
Film and Television, Theater

Work Environment
Indoors and outdoors, Primarily multiple locations

Minimum Education Level
Some postsecondary training

Salary Range
$200 per week to $400 per week

Certification or Licensing
None

Outlook
About as fast as the average

DOT
962

GOE
01.03.01

NOC
5227

Definition

The *production assistant* performs a variety of tasks for the producer and other staff members. He or she must be prepared to help out everywhere, ensuring that daily operations run as smoothly as possible. Some may perform substantive jobs, such as reviewing scripts, but others may primarily run errands. They must be willing to work hard and keep long hours at times, since tight production schedules require full days. An agreeable temperament and willingness to follow instructions and perform simple tasks are very important skills.

History

In the early twentieth century, as motion pictures were first developing, the roles of director and producer were combined in one person. European filmmakers such as Georges Melies and Leon Gaumont and New Yorker Edwin S. Porter directed, filmed, and produced very short movies. The first woman to become a director and producer was Alice Guy, who started the Solax Company in New York in 1910.

The film industry settled in Hollywood and began to consolidate in the first two decades of this century, as jobs were differentiated. Major studios assembled large staffs so all stages of production from conception to financing and directing could be performed within a single studio. Twentieth Century Fox, for example, would have producers, writers, directors, and actors on staff to choose from for each film. Small producers were forced out of business as major studios grew to have a monopoly on the industry.

In the 1950s the dominance of major studios in film production was curbed by an antitrust court decision, and more independent producers were able to find projects. Changes in the U.S. tax code made independent producing more profitable. At the same time, the growth of television provided new opportunities for producers. The industry is becoming increasingly international; many foreign-made films are now financed by Americans, and a number of American motion picture companies are under foreign ownership.

Currently many producers work on a project-by-project basis. The independent producer must be a good salesperson to market a project to a studio and to other financial backers. He or she will try to involve popular actors and actresses with the project from its inception in order to attract a studio's interest. Studios hire production assistants to facilitate the work of the producer and other staff members.

Nature of the Work

The work of a production assistant is not glamorous, but production is the best place to learn about the film and television industries. All hiring, casting, and decision making is done by members of production; they are involved with a project from the very beginning through its final stages. The producer is in charge—he or she is responsible for coordinating the activities of all employees involved in a production. Producers oversee the budget, and they have the final word on most decisions made for a film or television show.

The responsibilities of a production assistant may range from making sure the star has coffee in the morning to stopping street traffic so a director can film a scene. He or she may photocopy the script for actors, assist in setting up equipment, or perform other menial tasks. The best PAs know where to be at the right time to make themselves useful. Production can be stressful; time is money and mistakes can be very costly. An assistant must be prepared to handle unforeseen problems and smooth out difficulties. He or she should be prepared to help out as quickly as possible.

Duties may include keeping production files in order. These files will include contracts, budgets, page changes (old pages from a script that has been revised), and other records. The documents must be kept organized and accessible for whenever the producer may need them.

The assistant may also have to keep the producer's production folder in order and up to date. The production folder contains everything the producer needs to know about the production at a glance. It is particularly useful for times when a producer is on location away from the studio and cannot access the office files. The assistant must ensure that the folder includes the following: the shooting schedule, the most recent version of the budget, cast and crew lists with phone numbers, a phone sheet detailing all production-related phone calls the producer needs to make, and the up-to-date shooting script. As new versions of these forms are created, the PA will update the producer's folder and file the older versions for reference.

The production assistant may also be in charge of making sure that the producer gets the *dailies,* the film shot each day, wherever he is. The PA will have to schedule an hour or so in a producer's schedule to watch the dailies and to make related calls to discuss them with other staff members.

Requirements

There are no formal education requirements for production assistants. One's ultimate career goal should dictate education choices. If a student wishes to become a producer, he or she should take classes in film and theater as well as business. Formal training in production is available at some colleges and universities.

Production assistants must be willing to work long, demanding hours in order to be on hand for a long movie shoot. An agreeable personality and willingness to follow instructions and perform simple tasks are very important.

Opportunities for Experience & Exploration

There are many ways to gain experience with filmmaking. Some high schools have film clubs and classes in film or video. Experience in theater can also be useful. To learn more, a student can work as a volunteer for a local theater or a low-budget film project; these positions are often advertised in local trade publications.

Students interested in production work should read as much as possible about the film and television industry, starting at a school or public library. Trade journals can be very helpful as well; the two most prominent ones are *Hollywood Reporter* and *Daily Variety*. These resources will have information about production studios that will prove very useful for prospective PAs.

Methods of Entering

Interested students should seek internships, which may offer course credit if they are unpaid, by looking in trade journals and contacting film and television studios. Similarly, to find a position as a production assistant you should consult trade journals and contact studios. Since this is an entry-level position, opportunities will open as other assistants advance.

Advancement

A diligent production assistant will make contacts on the job that may help them advance into other jobs, such as that of line producer. A line producer works closely with the producer; he or she signs checks, advises on union rules, and negotiates deals with studio personnel. An associate producer performs similar work. To become a producer or director requires years of experience and hard work.

Employment Outlook

There will always be a need for assistants in film and television production. However, since it is such a good entry-level position for someone who wants to make connections and learn about the industry, competition for jobs can be tough. Production assistants will find employment anywhere a motion picture or television show is being filmed, but significant opportunities exist in Los Angeles and New York—the production hubs of the industry.

Earnings

Production assistants can expect to earn between $200 and $400 per week on average, and they work hard for their salary.

Conditions of Work

A film set is an exciting environment, but the production assistant may be treated poorly there. With a positive attitude, energy, and a desire to be useful, the PA will earn respect from the production department.

There are unwritten rules that should be followed. A production assistant who works for the producer or for the studio can be seen as an outsider in the eyes of the director and the creative team, so the PA should be respectful and well-behaved. This means you should be quiet, stay out of the way, and avoiding touching sets and equipment. If you behave as a guest, but remain helpful when needed, you will earn a good reputation that will be valuable for advancing your career.

The work environment will vary—the PA may be required on location, or may work mainly in the studio.

Sources of Additional Information

For information about colleges with film and television programs of study, please contact:

■ **American Film Institute**
PO Box 27999
2021 North Western Avenue
Los Angeles, CA 90027
Tel: 213-856-7600
WWW: http://www.afionline.org

For information about their Internship Directory or student membership, please contact:

United States Institute of Theater Technology
10 West 19th Street, Suite 5A
New York, NY 10011
Tel: 212-924-9088
WWW: http://www.culturenet.ca<\\>usitt

Producers Guild of America
400 South Beverly Drive
Beverly Hills, CA 90212
Tel: 310-557-0807

Screenwriters

School Subjects
Business, English (writing/literature)

Personal Interests
Film and Television, Writing

Work Environment
Primarily indoors, Primarily one location

Minimum Education Level
High school diploma

Salary Range
$15,000 to $600,000+

Certification or Licensing
None

Outlook
Faster than the average

DOT
131

GOE
01.01.02

NOC
5121

Definition

Screenwriters write scripts for entertainment, education, training, sales, and films. They may choose themes themselves, or they may write on a theme assigned by a producer or director, sometimes adapting plays or novels into screenplays. Screenwriting is an art, a craft, and a business. It is a career that requires imagination and creativity, the ability to tell a story using both dialogue and pictures, and the ability to negotiate with producers and studio executives.

History

In 1894, Thomas Edison (1847–1931) invented the kinetograph to take a series of pictures of actions staged specifically for the camera. In October of the same year, the first film opened at Hoyt's Theatre in New York. It was a series of acts performed by such characters as a strongman, a contortionist, and trained animals. Even in these earliest motion pictures, the plot or sequence of actions the film would portray was written down before filming began.

Newspaperman Roy McCardell was the first person to be hired for the specific job of writing for motion pictures. He wrote captions for photographs in an entertainment weekly. When he was employed by Biograph to write ten scenarios, or stories, at $10 apiece, it caused a flood of newspapermen to try their hand at screenwriting.

The early films, which ran only about a minute and were photographs of interesting movement, grew into story films, which ran between nine and fifteen minutes. The demand for original plots led to the development of story departments at each of the motion picture companies in the period from 1910 to 1915. The story departments were responsible for writing the stories and also for reading and evaluating material that came from outside sources. Stories usually came from writers, but some were purchased from actors on the lot. The actor Genevieve (Gene) Gauntier, was paid $20 per reel of film for her first scenarios.

There was a continuing need for scripts because usually a studio bought a story one month, filmed the next, and released the film the month after. Some of the most popular stories in these early films were Wild West tales and comedies.

Longer story films began to use titles, and as motion pictures became longer and more sophisticated, so did the titles. Around 1910, there was an average of 80 feet of title per 1000 feet of film. By 1926, the average increased to 250 feet of title per 1000 feet. The titles included dialogue, description, and historical background.

In 1920, the first Screen Writers Guild was established to ensure fair treatment of writers, and in 1927 the Academy of Motion Picture Arts and Sciences was formed, including a branch for writers. The first sound film, *The Jazz Singer,* was also produced in 1927. Screenwriting changed dramatically to adapt to the new technology.

From the 1950s to the 1980s, the studios gradually declined and more independent film companies and individuals were able to break into the motion picture industry. The television industry began to thrive in the 1950s, further increasing the number of opportunities for screenwriters. During the 1960s, people began to graduate from the first education programs developed specifically for screenwriting.

Today, most Americans have spent countless hours viewing programs on television and movie screens. Familiarity with these mediums has led many writers to attempt writing screenplays. This has created an intensely fierce marketplace with many more screenplays being rejected than accepted each year.

Nature of the Work

Screenwriters write dramas, comedies, soap operas, adventures, westerns, documentaries, newscasts, and training films. They may write original stories, or get inspiration from newspapers, magazines, or books. They may also write scripts for continuing television series. *Continuity writers* in broadcasting create station announcements, previews of coming shows, and advertising copy for local sponsors. *Broadcasting scriptwriters* usually work in a team, writing for a certain audience, to fill a certain time slot. *Motion picture writers* submit an original screenplay or adaptation of a book to a motion picture producer or studio. *Playwrights* submit their plays to drama companies for performance or try to get their work published in book form.

Screenwriters may work on a staff of writers and producers for a large company. Or they may work independently for smaller companies that hire only freelance production teams. Advertising agencies also hire writers, sometimes as staff, sometimes as freelancers.

Scripts are written in a two-column format, one column for dialogue and sound, the other for video instructions. One page of script equals about one minute of running time, though it varies. Each page has about 150 words and takes about twenty seconds to read. Screenwriters send a query letter outlining their idea before they submit a script to a production company. Then they send a standard release form and wait at least a month for a response. Studios buy many more scripts than are actually produced, and studios often will buy a script only with provisions that the original writer or another writer, will rewrite it to their specifications.

Requirements

There are no set educational requirements for screenwriters. A college degree is desirable, especially a liberal arts education that exposes the student to a wide range of subjects. Screenwriters must be able to create believable characters and develop a story. They must have technical skills, such as dialogue writing, creating plots, and doing research. Word processing skills are also helpful.

Opportunities for Experience & Exploration

One of the best ways to learn about screenwriting is to read and study scripts. It is advisable to watch a motion picture while simultaneously following the script. Literature and writing courses are necessary, and involvement in school or community theater is helpful. Many high schools and colleges offer specific courses in writing for television, movies, and the theater.

The International Television Association has local chapters throughout the United States, and many of them run a job hotline listing current opportunities. Students should read film industry publications, such as *Daily Variety, Hollywood Reporter,* and *The Hollywood Scriptwriter.* Independent Feature Project, a nonprofit support group, publishes a monthly newsletter for screenwriters, called *Montage.*

There are a number of books that give creative guidelines as well as technical information on how to write scripts, and how to negotiate with studios and producers. Three such books are *Successful Scriptwriting,* by Jurgen Wolff and Kerry Cox; *Best American Screenplays,* edited by Sam Thomas; and *Elements of Screenwriting,* by Irwin Blacker.

The Sundance Institute, a Utah-based production company, accepts unsolicited scripts from those who have read the Institute's submission guidelines. Every January they choose a few scripts and invite the writers to a five-day program of one-on-one sessions with professionals. The process is repeated in June, and also includes a videotaping of sections of chosen scripts. The Institute doesn't produce features, but they can often introduce writers to those who do. (For guidelines, send a self-addressed, stamped envelope with your request to The Sundance Institute, Production Building 7, Room 10, 4000 Warner Boulevard, Burbank, CA 91522.)

Most states offer grants for emerging and established screenwriters and other artists. Contact your state's Art Council for guidelines and application materials. In addition, several arts groups and associations hold annual contests for screenwriters. To find out more about screenwriting contests, consult a reference work such as the *Writer's Market.*

Students may try to get their work performed locally. A teacher may be able to help you submit your work to a local radio or television station or to a publisher of plays.

Methods of Entering

The first step to getting a screenplay produced is to write a letter to the script editor describing yourself, your training, and your work. Ask if the editors would be interested in reading one of your scripts. The screenwriter then prepares a synopsis or treatment of the screenplay, which is usually from one to ten pages. It should be in the form of a narrative short story, with little or no dialogue. Experienced writers submit their treatments to agents or production companies. Beginners, however, should write the entire screenplay, because if a studio or producer likes a treatment, they may buy it and then hire a proven screenwriter to write the script to their specifications.

Whether you are a beginning or experienced screenwriter, it is best to have an agent, since studios, producers and stars often return unsolicited manuscripts unopened to protect themselves from plagiarism charges. Agents provide access to studios and producers, interpret contracts, and negotiate deals.

After their first script is purchased, screenwriters join the Writers Guild of America. It is wise to register your script for $10 at the Writer's Guild. Although registration offers no legal protection, it is proof that on a specific date you came up with a particular idea, treatment, or script.

Advancement

Competition is stiff among screenwriters, and a beginner will find it difficult to break into the field. More opportunities become available as you gain experience and a reputation, but that is a process that can take many years. Rejection is a common occurrence in the field of screenwriting. Most successful screenwriters have had to send their screenplays to numerous production companies before they find one that likes their work.

Employment Outlook

There is intense competition in the television and motion picture industries. As cable television expands, however, new opportunities may emerge. Television networks continue to need new material, and new episodes for long-running series. Studios are always looking for new angles on action, adventure, horror, and comedy, especially romantic comedy stories. The demand for new screenplays should increase slightly in the next decade, but the number of screenwriters is growing at a faster rate. Writers will continue to find opportunities in advertising agencies and educational and training videos production houses.

Earnings

Film production budgets are tight and inflexible, so screenwriters should have an idea of the film's budget before writing the script. They need to work closely with the producer to be sure the script is shootable.

Fees have many variables. Generally a screenwriter will charge a minimum of $500 and add charges according to the number of drafts written (three is the norm); the number of meetings attended; the intended length of the motion picture; the intended use of the show; how much research is involved; and how long it will take to write the script. The screenwriter must also consider cowriters, deadlines, percent-of-profits versus money up-front, and video and foreign rights. A good development deal might pay $25,000 for a first draft, $10,000 for each of several rewrites, plus a bonus of two or three times that amount if filming begins, and a similar bonus if filming is completed. Sometimes writers negotiate for a percentage of movie profits or royalties.

Playwrights earn royalties on work published in book form and also receive a percentage of box-office receipts. The Dramatists Guild sets professional standards for playwrights and guarantees authors' rights. Script fees are set by the Writers Guild of America.

Motion picture screenwriters can earn a minimum of $54,266 for a screenplay and treatment. An established motion picture screenwriter can earn $100,000 to $600,000 per screenplay. Screenwriters who develop a screenplay for a two-hour network television program can earn a minimum of $46,505. A writer for a half-hour prime-time situation comedy can earn $135,627 per story or teleplay. Staff writers for a TV show can earn from $2,018 to $4,804 per week for a guaranteed number of weeks.

Conditions of Work

Screenwriters who choose to freelance have the freedom to write when and where they choose. They must be persistent and patient—only one in twenty to thirty purchased or optioned screenplays is produced.

Screenwriters who work on the staff of a large company, for a television series, or under contract to a motion picture company, may share writing duties with others.

Screenwriters who do not live in Hollywood or New York will likely have to travel to attend script conferences. They may even have to relocate for several weeks while a show is being prepared. Busy periods before and during film production are followed by long periods of inactivity and solitude. This forces many screenwriters, especially those just getting started in the field, to work other jobs and pursue other careers while they develop their talent and craft.

Sources of Additional Information

■ **Dramatists Guild**
234 West 44th Street
New York, NY 10036-9366
Tel: 212-398-9366

■ **Writers Guild of America, East**
555 West 57th Street
New York, NY 10019
Tel: 212-767-7800

■ **Writers Guild of America, West**
8955 Beverly Boulevard
Los Angeles, CA 90048
Tel: 310-550-1000

Singers

School Subjects
Music, Speech

Personal Interests
Entertaining, Music

Work Environment
Primarily indoors, Primarily multiple locations

Minimum Education Level
High school diploma

Salary Range
$6,900 to $70,000

Certification or Licensing
None

Outlook
About as fast as the average

DOT
152

GOE
01.04.03

NOC
5133

Definition

Professional *singers* perform opera, gospel, blues, rock, jazz, folk, classical, country, and other musical genres, before an audience or in recordings. Singers are musicians who use their voices as their instruments, and may perform as part of a band, choir, or other musical ensembles, or solo, whether with or without musical accompaniment.

History

"Song is man's sweetest joy," said a poet in the eighth century BCE. Singers are those who use their voices as instruments of sound and are capable of relating music that touches the soul. The verb *to sing* is related to the Greek term *omphe,* which

157

means "voice." In general, singing is related to music and thus to the Muses, the goddesses of ancient Greek religion who are said to watch over the arts and are sources of inspiration.

Singing, or vocal performance, is considered the mother of all music, which is thought of as an international language. In human history, before musical instruments were ever devised, there was always the voice, which has had the longest and most significant influence on the development of all musical forms and materials that have followed.

A precise, formal history of the singing profession is not feasible, for singing evolved in different parts of the world and in diverse ways at various times. A forty-thousand-year-old cave painting in France suggests the earliest evidence of music; the painting shows a man playing a musical bow and dancing behind several reindeer. Most civilizations have had legends suggesting that gods created song, and many myths suggest that nymphs have passed the art of singing to us. The Chinese philosopher Confucius (551-478 BCE) considered music to be a significant aspect of a moral society, with its ability to portray emotions as diverse as joy and sorrow, anger and love.

There are certain differences between Eastern and Western music. In general, music of Middle Eastern civilizations has tended to be more complex in its melodies (although music from the Far East is often simplistic). Western music has been greatly influenced by the organized systems of musical scales of ancient Greece and has evolved through various eras, which were rich and enduring but can be defined in general terms. The first Western musical era is considered to have been the medieval period (c. 850–1450), when the earliest surviving songs were written by twelfth-century French troubadours and German minnesingers; these poet-musicians sang of love, nature, and religion. The next periods include the Renaissance (c. 1450–1600), during which the musical attitude was one of calm and self-restraint; the Baroque (c. 1600–1750), a time of extravagance, excitement, and splendor; the Classical (c. 1750–1820), a return to simplicity; and the Romantic (c. 1820–1950), which represents a time of strong emotional expression and fascination with nature.

In primitive societies of the past and present, music has played more of a ritualistic, sacred role. In any case, singing has been considered an art form for thousands of years, powerfully influencing the evolution of societies. It is a large part of our leisure environment, our ceremonies, and our religions; the power of song has even been said to heal illness and sorrow. In antiquity, musicians tended to have more than one role, serving as composer, singer, and instrumentalist at the same time. They also tended to be found in the highest levels of society and to take part in events such as royal ceremonies, funerals, and processions.

The function of singing as an interpretive, entertaining activity was established relatively recently. Opera had its beginnings in the late sixteenth century in Italy and matured during the following centuries in other European countries. The rise of the professional singer (also referred to as the vocal virtuoso because of the expert talent involved) occurred in the seventeenth and eighteenth centuries. At this time, musical composers began to sing to wider audiences, who called for further expression and passion in singing.

Throughout the periods of Western music, the various aspects of song have changed along with general musical developments. Such aspects include melody, harmony, rhythm, tempo, dynamics, texture, and other characteristics. The structures of song are seemingly unlimited and have evolved from plainsong and madrigal, chanson and chorale, opera and cantata, folk and motet, anthem and drama, to today's expanse of pop, rock, country, rap, and so on. The development of radio, television, motion pictures, and various types of recordings (LP records, cassettes, and compact discs) has had a great effect on the singing profession, creating smaller audiences for live performances yet larger and larger audiences for recorded music.

Nature of the Work

Essentially, singers are employed to perform music with their voices by using their knowledge of vocal sound and delivery, harmony, melody, and rhythm. They put their individual vocal styles into the songs they sing, and they interpret music accordingly. The inherent sounds of the voices in a performance play a significant part in how a song will affect an audience; this essential aspect of a singer's voice is known as its tone.

Classical singers are usually categorized according to the range and quality of their voices, beginning with the highest singing voice, the soprano, and ending with the lowest, the bass; voices in between include mezzo soprano, contralto, tenor, and baritone. Singers perform either alone (in which case they are referred to as soloists) or as members of an ensemble, or group. They sing by either following a score, which is the printed musical text, or by memorizing the material. Also, they may sing either with or without instrumental accompaniment; it is called performing a cappella when they sing without it. In opera—actually plays set to music—singers perform the various roles, much as actors, interpreting the drama with their voice to the accompaniment of a symphony orchestra.

Classical singers may perform a variety of musical styles, or specialize in a specific period; they may give recitals, or perform as members of an ensemble. Classical singers generally undergo years of voice training and instruction in musical theory. They develop their vocal technique, and learn how to project without harming their voice, which is their instrument, after all. Classical singers rarely use a microphone when they sing; nonetheless, their voices must be heard above the orchestra. Because classical singers often perform music from many different languages, they learn how to pronounce these languages, and often how to speak them as well. Those who are involved in opera work for opera companies in major cities throughout the country and often travel extensively. Some classical singers also perform in other musical areas.

Professional singers tend to perform in a certain chosen style of music, such as jazz, rock, or blues, among many others. Many singers pursue careers that will lead them to perform for coveted recording contracts, on concert tours, and for television and motion pictures. Others perform in rock, pop, country, gospel, or folk groups, singing in concert halls, nightclubs, and churches and at social gatherings and for small studio recordings. Whereas virtuosos, classical artists who are expertly skilled in their singing style, tend to perform traditional pieces that have been handed down through hundreds of years, singers in other areas often perform popular, current pieces, and often songs that they themselves have composed.

Another style of music in which formal training is often helpful is jazz. *Jazz singers* learn phrasing, breathing, and vocal techniques; often, the goal of a jazz singer is to become as much a part of the instrumentation as the piano, saxophone, trumpet, or trombone. Many jazz singers perform "scat" singing, in which the voice is used in an improvisational way much like any other instrument.

Folk singers perform songs that may be many years old, or they may write their own songs. Folk singers generally perform songs that express a certain cultural tradition; while some folk singers specialize in their own or another culture, others may sing songs from a great variety of cultural and musical traditions. In the United States, folk singing is particularly linked to the acoustic guitar, and many singers accompany themselves while singing.

A cappella singing, which is singing without musical accompaniment, takes many forms. A cappella music may be a part of classical music; it may also be a part of folk music, as in the singing of barbershop quartets. Another form, called doo-wop, is closely linked to rock and rhythm and blues music.

Gospel music, which evolved in the United States, is a form of sacred music; *gospel singers* generally sing as part of a choir, accompanied by an organ, or other musical instruments, but may also be performed a cappella. Many popular singers began their careers as singers in church and gospel choirs before entering jazz, pop, blues, or rock.

Rock singers generally require no formal training whatsoever. Rock music is a very broad term encompassing many different styles of music, such as heavy metal, punk, rap, rhythm & blues, rockabilly, techno, and many others. Many popular rock singers cannot even sing. But rock singers learn to express themselves and their music, developing their own phrasing and vocal techniques. Rock singers usually sing as part of a band, or with a backing band to accompany them. Rock singers usually sing with microphones so that they can be heard above the amplified instruments around them.

All singers practice and rehearse their songs and music. Some singers read from music scores while performing; others perform from memory. Yet all must gain an intimate knowledge of their music, so that they can best convey its meanings and feelings to their audience. Singers must also exercise their voices even when not performing. Some singers perform as featured soloists and artists. Other perform as part of a choir, or as backup singers adding harmony to the lead singer's voice.

Requirements

As noted above, many singers require no formal training in order to sing. However, those interested in becoming classical or jazz singers should begin learning and honing their talent when they are quite young. Vocal talent can be recognized in grade school students and even in younger children. In general, however, these early years are a time of vast development and growth in singing ability. Evident changes occur in boys' and girls' voices when they are around twelve to fourteen years old, during which time their vocal cords go through a process of lengthening and thickening. Boys' voices tend to change much more so than girls' voices, although both genders should be provided with challenges that will help them achieve their talent goals. Young students should learn about breath control and why it is necessary; they should learn to follow a conductor, including the relationship between hand and baton motions and the dynamics of the music; and they should learn about musical concepts such as tone, melody, harmony, and rhythm.

During the last two years of high school, aspiring singers should have a good idea of what classification they are in, according to the range and quality of their voices: soprano, alto, contralto, tenor, baritone, or bass. These categories indicate the resonance of the voice; soprano being the highest and lightest, bass being the lowest and heaviest. Students should take part in voice classes, choirs, and ensembles. In addition, students should continue their studies in English, writing, social studies, foreign language, and other electives in music, theory, and performance.

There tend to be no formal educational requirements for those who wish to be singers. However, formal education is valuable, especially in younger years. Some students know early in their lives that they want to be singers and are ambitious enough to continue to practice and learn. These students are often advised to attend high schools that are specifically geared toward combined academic and intensive arts education in music, dance, and theater. Such schools can provide valuable preparation and guidance for those who plan to pursue professional careers in the arts. Admission is usually based on results from students' auditions as well as academic testing.

Many find it worthwhile and fascinating to continue their study of music and voice in a liberal arts program at a college or university. Similarly, others attend schools of higher education that are focused specifically on music, such as the Juilliard School in New York. Such an intense program would include a multidisciplinary curriculum of composition and performance, as well as study and appreciation of the history, development, variety, and potential advances of music. In this type of program, a student would earn a bachelor of arts degree. To earn a bachelor of science degree in music, one would study musicology, which concerns the history, literature, and cultural background of music; the music industry, which will prepare one for not only singing but also marketing music and other business aspects; and professional performance. Specific music classes in a typical four-year liberal arts program would include such courses as introduction to music, music styles and structures, harmony, theory of music, elementary and advanced auditory training, music history, and individual instruction.

In addition to learning at schools, many singers are taught by private singing teachers and voice coaches, who help to develop and refine students' voices. Many aspiring singers take courses at continuing adult education centers, where they can take advantage of courses in beginning and advanced singing, basic vocal techniques, voice coaching, and vocal performance workshops. When one is involved in voice training, he or she must learn about good articulation and breath control, which are very important qualities for all singers. Performers must take care of their voices and keep their lungs in good condition. Voice training, whether as part of a college curriculum or in private study, is useful to many singers, not only for classical and opera singers, but also for jazz singers and for those interested in careers in musical theater. Many professional singers who have already "made it" continue to take voice lessons throughout their careers.

In other areas of music, learning to sing and becoming a singer is often a matter of desire, practice, and an inborn love and talent for singing. Learning to play a musical instrument is often extremely helpful in learning to sing and to read and write music. Sometimes it is not even necessary to have a "good" singing voice. Many singers in rock music have less-than-perfect voices, and rap artists do not really sing at all. But these singers learn to use their voice in ways that nonetheless provides good expression to their songs, music, and ideas.

Opportunities for Experience & Exploration

Anyone who is interested in pursuing a career as a singer should obviously have a love for music. Listen to recordings as often as possible, and get an understanding of the types of music that you enjoy. Singing, alone or with family and friends, is one of the most natural ways to explore music and develop a sense of your own vocal style. Join music clubs at school, as well as the school band if it does vocal performances. In addition, take part in school drama productions that involve musical numbers.

Older students interested in classical music careers could contact trade associations such as the American Guild of Musical Artists, as well as read such trade journals such as *Hot Line News,* which covers news about singers (and other types of musicians) and their employment needs and opportunities. For information and news about very popular singers, read *Billboard* magazine, which can be purchased at many local bookshops and newsstands. Those who already know what type of music they wish to sing should audition for roles in community musical productions or contact trade groups that offer competitions. For example, the Central Opera Service can provide information on competitions, apprentice programs, and performances for young singers interested in opera.

There are many summer programs offered throughout the United States for high school students interested in singing and other performing arts. For example, Stanford University offers its Stanford Jazz Workshop each summer for students who are at least twelve years old. It offers activities in instrumental and vocal music, as well as recreation in swimming, tennis, and volleyball. For college students who are eighteen years and older, the jazz workshop has a number of job positions available. For more information about the program, contact the university at Box 11291, Stanford, CA 94309.

Another educational institute that presents a summer program is Boston University's Tanglewood Institute, which is geared especially toward very talented and ambitious students between the ages of fifteen and eighteen. It offers sessions in chorus, musical productions, chamber music, classical music, ensemble, instrumental, and vocal practice. Arts and culture field trips are also planned. College students who are at least twenty years old can apply for available jobs at the summer Tanglewood programs. For more information, contact Boston University, Lenox, MA 01240.

Students interested in other areas of singing can begin while still in high school, or even sooner. Many gospel singers, for example, start singing with their local church group at an early age. Many high school students form their own bands, playing rock, country, or jazz,

163

and can gain experience performing before an audience, and even being paid to perform at school parties and other social functions.

Methods of Entering

Because there are so many different environments in which singers can be employed, including local lounges, bars, cafes, radio and television, theater productions, cruise ships, resorts, hotels, casinos, large concert tours, and opera companies, there is no single correct way of entering the profession. It is recommended that aspiring singers explore the avenues that interest them, continuing to apply and audition for whatever medium suits them. Singing is an extremely creative profession, and singers must learn to be creative and resourceful in the business matters of finding "gigs."

Many singers hire agents, who usually receive a percentage of the singer's earnings for finding them appropriate performance contracts. Others are employed primarily as studio singers, which means that they do not perform for live audiences but rather record their singing in studios for albums, radio, television, and motion pictures.

Advancement

In the singing profession and the music industry in general, the nature of the business is such that you can consider yourself to have "made it" when you get steady, full-time work. A measure of advancement is in how well known and respected the singer becomes in his or her field, which in turn influences their earnings. In most areas, particularly classical music, only the most talented and persistent singers make it to the top of their profession. In other areas, success may be largely a matter of luck and perseverance. A singer on Broadway, for example, may begin as a member of the chorus, and eventually become a featured singer. On the other hand, those who have a certain passion for their work and accept their career position tend to enjoy working in local performance centers, nightclubs, and other musical environments.

Also, many experienced singers who have had formal training will become voice teachers. Reputable schools such as Juilliard consider it a plus when a student can say that he or she has studied with a master.

Employment Outlook

Any employment forecast for singers will most probably emphasize one factor that plays an important role in the availability of jobs: competition. Because so many people pursue musical careers and because there tend to be no formal requirements for employment in this industry (the main qualification is talent), competition is most often very strong.

According to the U.S. Department of Labor, available jobs for singers, as for musicians in general, are expected to grow slowly into the next century. However, others foresee growth in the entertainment industry during the next decade, which will create jobs for singers and other performers. Because of the nature of this work, positions tend to be temporary and part-time; in fact, of all members of the American Federation of Musicians, fewer than 2 percent work full-time in their singing careers. Thus, it is often advised that those who are intent on pursuing a singing career keep in mind the varied fields other than performance in which their interest in music can be beneficial, such as composition, education, broadcasting, therapy, and community arts management.

Those intent on pursuing singer careers in rock, jazz, and other popular forms should understand the keen competition they will face. There are thousands of singers all hoping to make it; only a very few actually succeed. However, there are many opportunities to perform in local cities and communities, and those with a genuine love of singing and performing should also possess a strong sense of commitment and dedication to their art.

Earnings

As with many occupations in the performing arts, earnings for singers are highly dependent on one's professional reputation and thus cover a wide range. To some degree, pay is also related to educational background (as it relates to how well one has been trained) and geographic location of performances. In certain situations, such as singing for phonograph recordings, pay is dependent on the number of minutes of finished music (for instance, an hour's pay will be given for each three and a half minutes of recorded song).

Singing is often considered a glamorous occupation. However, because it attracts so many professionals, competition for positions is very high. Only a small proportion of those who aspire to be singers achieve glamorous jobs and extremely lucrative contracts. Famous opera singers, for example earn $8,000 and more for each performance. Singers in an opera chorus earn between $600 and $800 per week. Classical soloists can receive between $2,000 and $3,000 per

165

performance, while choristers may receive around $70 per performance. For rock singers, earnings can be far higher. Within the overall group of professional singers, studio and opera singers tend to earn salaries that are well respected in the industry; their opportunities for steady, long-term contracts tend to be better than for singers in other areas.

In general, starting salaries could be as low as $6,900 per year or even far less. Average salaries tend to be around $26,000; the top earners in studio and opera earn an average of $70,000 per year, though some earn much more. Rock singers may begin by playing for drinks and meals only; if successful, they may earn tens of thousands of dollars for a single performance. Singers on cruise ships generally earn between $750 and $2,000 per week, although these figures can vary considerably. Also, many singers supplement their performance earnings by working at other positions, such as teaching at schools or giving private lessons or even working at jobs unrelated to singing. Full-time teachers in high school earn an average of $26,000 per year, while those at colleges earn an average of $35,500 per year.

Because singers rarely work for a single employer, they generally receive no benefits, and must provide their own health insurance and retirement planning.

Conditions of Work

The environments in which singers work tend to vary greatly, depending on such factors as type of music involved and location of performance area. Professional singers often work in the evenings and during weekends, and many are frequently required to travel. Many singers who are involved in popular productions such as in opera, rock, and country music work in large cities such as New York, Las Vegas, Chicago, Los Angeles, and Nashville. Stamina and endurance are needed to keep up with the hours of rehearsals and performances, which can be long; work schedules are very often erratic, varying from job to job.

Many singers are members of trade unions, which represent them in matters such as wage scales and fair working conditions. Vocal performers who sing for studio recordings are represented by the American Federation of Television and Radio Artists; solo opera singers, solo concert singers, and choral singers are members of the American Guild of Musical Artists.

Sources of Additional Information

■ **American Federation of Musicians of the United States and Canada**
Paramount Building
1501 Broadway, Suite 600
New York, NY 10036
Tel: 212-869-1330

■ **American Federation of Television and Radio Artists**
260 Madison Avenue
New York, NY 10016
Tel: 212-532-0800

■ **Musicians National Hot Line Association**
277 East 6100 South
Salt Lake City, UT 84107

■ **National Association of Schools of Music**
11250 Roger Bacon Drive, Suite 21
Reston, VA 22090
Tel: 703-437-0700

■ **Opera America**
1156 15th Street, Suite 810
Washington, DC 20005-1704
Tel: 202-293-4466

Songwriters

Definition

Songwriters write the words and music for songs, including songs for recordings, advertising jingles, and theatrical performances. We hear the work of songwriters every day, and yet most songwriters remain anonymous, even if a song's performer is famous. Many songwriters, of course, perform their own songs.

History

Music has always been an important form of human communication. In early society, before writing was invented, societies preserved their history and cultural and religious traditions through oral literature. Among the most famous examples of this are the *Illiad* and the *Odyssey* by Homer. Because these early stories were often long and complex, they followed set patterns of rhythms and repeated phrases that made it easier for the reciter, or "singer" to remember. Often, songs played a part in the telling of a story, providing entertainment while also making it easier to memorize the words to a story. Other forms of oral literature include folktales, chants, and nursery rhymes. Today, many societies that have not developed a written language, particularly in Africa and among native American tribes, still preserve their history, traditions, and culture through the use of songs and stories.

As societies developed writing, they also developed systems of musical notation, so that the melodies to a song could remain consistent no matter who was singing. An example of early musical notation is that still used for reciting the Jewish Torah. Musical instruments were also developed, and soon songwriting included writing the words and the musical accompaniment for a song.

Many styles of music were created in every part of the world. In Western society, early songs were often religious in nature, but from the beginning, songs have also been written solely for entertainment. In tenth-century Europe, minstrels were traveling entertainers who sang, played music, danced, as well as juggled and did acrobatics. Beginning in the twelfth century, minstrels provided musical accompaniment as troubadours composed and sang poems of courtly love. Many of the troubadours' manuscripts, containing the words and music to their songs, survive today.

Ballads also formed a part of the culture of many societies. These were poems, usually sung, that presented a dramatic story set to music. Ballads grew out of the oral literature of the Medieval period, and functioned much as newspapers and especially the tabloids function today, often telling stories of current events such as murders, acts of heroism and danger, and other dramatically intense themes. Ballads could often be highly melodramatic and sentimental, in their words as well as in their melodies. By the eighteenth century, ballads were printed on large sheets, called broadsides, that gave the words as well as the tune. These were sold for a penny, and became known as penny ballads.

Songwriting also played an important part in the growth of the United States. The early pioneers wrote songs as a way to relax. Some of the difficult experiences of traveling, fighting over land, farming, and hunting for food were put into words by early songwriters, and the words to set to music, for the guitar or banjo, piano, or other instruments. Francis Scott Key (1780?–1843) became famous for writing the words to the "Star Spangled Banner," set to a popular drinking tune.

Toward the end of the nineteenth century, sheet music was sold by dozens and even hundreds of publishing companies, centered in New York City in what became known as Tin Pan Alley. This name was coined by a songwriter and journalist named Monroe Rosenfeld, referring to the sounds of many voices and pianos coming from the open windows of the street where many of the music publishers were located. By the 1880s, sheet music sold in the millions; most songs were introduced on the stages of musical theater, vaudeville, and burlesque shows. A song could become quite popular, making the songwriter famous. Radio became an important medium for introducing new songs in the 1920s, followed by the introduction of sound movies in the 1930s. Sheet music became less important as musical recordings were introduced. This presented difficulties for the songwriter and publisher, because the sales of sheet music were easier to control. In the 1940s, the first associations for protecting the rights of the songwriters and publishers were formed; among the benefits songwriters received were royalties for each time a song they had written was recorded, performed, or played on the radio or in film. Many songwriters became quite famous. Famous songwriters include Richard Rodgers (1902–79) and Lorenz Hart (1895–1943), Cole Porter (1891–1964), George (1898–1937) and Ira (1896–1983) Gershwin, Sammy Kahn, Jerome Kern (1885–1945), and Irving Berlin (1888–1989). Their songs were in great demand by singers, musicians, musical theater, and others. Often, songwriters worked in teams, with one member, the lyricist, writing the words to a song, and the other member of the team composing the music.

Tin Pan Alley was not the only type of popular song. Country music, which had its origins in the 1920s and was derived from the British, Irish, and Scottish folk music traditions, became popular through large parts of the country. Eventually, the country music industry settled in Nashville, Tennessee, which continues to be one of the major points of the songwriting industry today.

The introduction of radio, and later, television created a new demand for songwriters: the advertising jingle. Perhaps more than any other kind of advertising, a jingle could capture the attention of the consumer, and many jingles were nearly as well known as popular songs.

By the 1950s, Tin Pan Alley no longer referred to a specific area in New York but was used nationwide to denote popular songs in general, and especially a type of simple melody and sentimental and often silly lyric that dominated the pop music industry. The rise of rock and roll music in the 1950s put an end to Tin Pan Alley's dominance. New styles of music emerged, and new songwriters and songwriting teams emerged into prominence. The famous team of Leiber and Stoller created many of the most well-known songs of the early rock years, especially those performed by Elvis Presley (1935–77). Carl Perkins (born 1932), who was also a singer and musician, created a number of songs that continue to define the 50s era. Many performers began to write their own songs as well, a trend that became particularly important in the 1960s. In the late 1970s, a new type of songwriting emerged. Rap music, featuring words chanted over a musical background, seemed to bring songwriting full circle, back to the oral traditions of its origins.

Today, songwriters continue to create songs for the many different kinds of contemporary music. Songwriters also create songs for advertising on television and radio. Television, film, and video also employ songwriters to create the themes for a new show, series, movie, or program. Songwriters compose music for marching bands and for musical theater. Some songwriters are even called upon to create national anthems.

Nature of the Work

There are many different ways to write a song. A song may begin with a few words—the lyric—or with a few notes of a melody, or a song may be suggested by an idea, theme, or product. A song may come about in a flash of inspiration, or may be developed slowly over a long period of time. Songwriters may work alone, or as part of a team, in which one person concentrates on the lyrics while another person concentrates on the music. Sometimes there may be several or even many people working on the same song.

Most songwriters work freelance, competing for contracts to write songs for a particular artist, television show, video program, or for contracts with musical publishers and advertising agencies. They will meet with clients to determine the nature of the project and to get an idea of what kind of music the client seeks, the budget for the project, the time in which the project is expected to be completed, and in what form the work is to be submitted. Many songwriters work under contract with one or more music publishing houses. Usually, they must fulfill a certain quota of new songs each year. These songwriters receive a salary, called an advance or draw, which is often paid by the week. Once a song has been published, the money earned by the song goes to pay back the songwriter's draw. A percentage of the money earned by the song over and above the amount of the draw goes to the songwriter as a royalty. Other songwriters are employed by so-called "jingle houses," that is, companies that supply music for advertising commercials. Whereas most songwriters work in their own homes or offices, these songwriters work at the jingle house's offices. Film, television, and video production studios may also employ songwriters on their staff.

Most popular songs require words, or lyrics, and some songwriters may concentrate on writing the words to a song. These songwriters are called *lyricists*. Events, experiences, or emotions may inspire a lyricist to write lyrics. A lyricist may also be contracted to write the words for a jingle, a musical, or adapt the words for an existing song for another project. A lyricist may write down several versions of the lyrics. Sometimes one version is a rhyming poem while the other reads like prose. Some song lyrics tell a complete story, while others may simply express one idea or feeling.

Some songwriters do no more than write the words to a potential song, and leave it to others to develop a melody and musical accompaniment for the words. They may sell the words to a music publisher, or work in a team to create a finished song from the lyric. Some lyricists specialize in writing the words for advertising jingles. They are usually employed by advertising agencies and may work on several different products at once, often under pressure of a deadline.

In songwriting teams, one member may be a lyricist, while the other member is a *composer*. The development of a song can be a highly collaborative process. The composer might suggest topics for the song to the lyricist; the lyricist might suggest a melody to the composer. Other times, the composer plays a musical piece for the lyricist, and the lyricist tries to create lyrics to fit with that piece.

Composers for popular music generally have a strong background in music, and often in performing music as well. They must have an understanding of many musical styles, so that they can develop the music that will fit a project's needs. Composers work with a variety of musical and electronic equipment, including computers, to produce and record their music. They develop the different parts for the different musical instruments needed to play the song. They also work with musicians who will play and record the song, and the composer conducts or otherwise directs the musicians as the song is played.

Songwriters, composers, and musicians often make use of MIDI (musical instrument digital interface) technology to produce sounds through synthesizers, drum machines, and samplers. These sounds are usually controlled by a computer, and the composer or songwriter can mix, alter, and refine the sounds using mixing boards and computer software. Like analog or acoustic instruments, which produce sounds as a string or reed or drum head vibrates with air, MIDI creates digital "vibrations" that can produce sounds similar to acoustic instruments or highly unusual sounds invented by the songwriter himself. Synthesizers and other sound-producing machines may each have their own keyboard or playing mechanism, or be linked through one or more keyboards. They may also be controlled through the computer, or with other types of controls, such as a guitar controller, which plays like a guitar, or foot controls. The songwriter then selects which synthesizer or machine he will be "playing." Songs can be stored in the computer, or transferred to tape or compact disc. MIDI technology has become increasingly important in the music industry, and songwriters should have some knowledge and experience working with it.

Songwriters, whether composers or lyricists or both, may work with singers and musicians as well. For example, a singer may be working on a special concert or recording and request a new song from the songwriter. The songwriter works with the singer to develop a song that works well with the singer's voice and vocal style, or lyrics that fit a certain theme.

Many, if not most, songwriters combine both the work of a lyricist and the work of a composer. Often, a songwriter will perform his or her own songs as well, whether as a singer, a member of a band, or both.

For most songwriters, writing a song is only the first part of their job. After a song is written, songwriters usually produce a "demo" of the song, so that the client or potential purchaser of the song can hear how it sounds. Songwriters contract with recording studios, studio musicians, and recording engineers to produce a version of the song. The songwriter then submits the song to a publishing house, record company, recording artist, film studio, or others, who will then decide if the song is appropriate for their needs. Often, a songwriter will produce several versions of a song, or submit several different songs for a particular project. There is always a chance that one, some, or all of their songs will be rejected.

Requirements

There are no real requirements for entering the field of songwriting. All songwriters, however, will benefit from musical training, including musical theory and musical notation. Learning to play one or more instruments, such as the piano or guitar, will be especially helpful in writing songs. Not all songwriters need to be able to sing, but this is helpful. For those interested in becoming lyricists, a strong knowledge of English and creative writing will be useful. A flair for the creative use of words is a useful talent for all songwriters.

Songwriting is an extremely competitive field. Despite a lack of formal educational requirements, prospective songwriters are encouraged to continue their education through high school and preferably toward a college degree. Much of the musical training a songwriter needs, however, can also be learned informally.

In general, a prospective songwriter should have a background in music theory, and in arrangement and orchestration for multiple instruments. They should be able to read music, and be able to write it in the proper musical notation. Songwriters should have a good sense of the sounds each type of musical instrument produces, alone and in combination. Understanding harmony is important, as well as a proficiency in or understanding of a variety of styles of music, that is, for example, what makes rock different from reggae, blues, or jazz. Studies in music history will also help develop this understanding.

On the technical side, a songwriter should understand the various features, capabilities, and requirements of modern recording techniques. They should be familiar with MIDI and computer technology, as these play an important role in composing, playing, and recording music today.

Other parts of songwriting cannot really be learned, but are a matter of inborn talent. A creative imagination, and the ability to invent melodies and combine melodies into a song are essential parts of a songwriting career. As songwriters become more familiar with their own talents, and with songwriting, they learn to develop and enhance these creative skills.

Songwriters should be able to work in isolation, often for long periods of time. Yet they must also be able to work with a team, including other songwriters, publishers, producers, musicians, and recording engineers and personnel. Finally, songwriters must develop a strong sense of patience. Writing a song may take a long time, and songwriters, as with most creative fields, often undergo periods of frustration when work on a song becomes difficult, or when their inspiration temporarily fades.

Most songwriters are self-employed, and should gain an understanding of basic business. Because most songwriters do not work full-time in this field, songwriters should gain the skills and education to find work in related or unrelated fields while they pursue their songwriting careers.

Professional songwriters should join one or more of the many organizations, such as BMI, ASCAP, and SESAC, which represent songwriters and protect their rights. These organizations often offer songwriting workshops and seminars, and also keep track of royalties that songwriters receive each time a song they wrote is recorded or played.

Opportunities for Experience & Exploration

The simplest way to gain experience in songwriting is to learn to play a musical instrument, especially the piano or guitar, and to invent your own songs. Joining a rock group is a way to gain experience writing music for several musicians. Most schools and communities have orchestras, bands, and choruses that are open to performers. Working on a student-written musical show is ideal training for the future songwriter. Language skills can be honed in English and foreign-language classes in high school and college, writing poetry, and by working on student literary magazines.

Students can also gain experience working with MIDI technology and computer-controlled music and recording equipment. Many schools feature electronic music laboratories. Students who own their own computers can also invest in software, keyboards, and other devices that will allow them to experiment with sounds, recording, and writing and composing their own songs. While much of this equipment is highly expensive, there are plenty of affordable keyboards, drum machines, and software available today.

There are several organizations that help lyricists, songwriters, and composers. The National Academy of Songwriters offers weekly song evaluation workshops in California. The Nashville Songwriters Association International offers workshops, seminars, and other services, as well as giving annual awards to songwriters. The Songwriters and Lyricists Club in New York provides contacts for songwriters with music-business professionals. These, and other organizations, offer songwriting workshops and other training seminars.

There are also many books on the different aspects of songwriting and the music and recording industry. Recommended readings include: David Ewen's *American Songwriters: One Hundred Forty-Six Biographies of America's Greatest Popular Composers and Lyricists* and *The Craft of Lyric Writing* by Sheila Davis.

Many colleges and universities with music departments offer degree programs in music. Some community colleges also have courses in songwriting.

Methods of Entering

Songwriting is a very competitive career and difficult to break into for a beginner. The number of high-paying projects is limited. Often, beginning songwriters start their careers writing music for themselves or as part of a musical group. They may also offer their services to student films, student and local theater productions, church groups, and other religious and nonprofit organizations, often for free or for a low fee.

Many songwriters get their start while performing their own music in clubs and other places; they may be approached by a music publisher, who contracts them for a number of songs. Other songwriters record demos of their songs and try to interest record companies and music publishers. Some songwriters organize showcase performances, hiring a local club or hall and inviting music industry people to hear their work. Songwriters may have to approach many companies and publishers before they find one willing to buy their songs. A great deal of making a success in songwriting is in developing contacts with people active in the music industry.

Some songwriters get their start in one of the few entry-level positions available. Songwriters aspiring to become composers for film and television can find work as orchestrators or copyists in film houses. Other songwriters may find work for music agents and publishers, which will give them an understanding of the industry and increase their contacts in the industry, as they develop their songwriting skills.

Those interested in specializing in advertising jingles may find entry-level work as *music production assistants* with a jingle house. At first, such jobs may involve making coffee, doing paperwork, and other clerical tasks. As the assistant gains more exposure to the process of creating music, they may begin in basic areas of music production, or assist experienced songwriters.

Advancement

It is important for a songwriter to develop a strong portfolio of work, and a reputation for professionalism. Songwriters who establish a reputation for the quality of their work will receive larger and higher-paying projects as their careers proceed. They may be contracted to score major motion pictures, or to write songs for major recording artists. Ultimately, they may be able not only to support themselves on their songwriting alone, but also have the ability to pick and choose the projects they will work on.

In order to continue to grow with the music industry, songwriters must be tuned into new musical styles and trends. They must also keep up with developments in music technology. A great deal of time is spend making and maintaining contacts with others in the music industry.

Songwriters specializing in jingles and other commercial products may eventually start up their own jingle house. Other songwriters, especially those who have written a number of hit songs, may themselves become recording artists.

A hit song can make a songwriter quite wealthy. They will continue to receive residuals each year for their songs. A song such as "White Christmas," originally made famous by Bing Crosby (1904–77) and which has become one of the most-recorded songs of all time, has earned many millions of dollars. The songs of the Beatles, now owned by Michael Jackson (born 1958), and the songs of Buddy Holly (1936-1959), now owned by Paul McCartney (born 1942), are also worth many millions of dollars. Another example of songwriting success is that of Mick Jagger (born 1944) and Keith Richards of the Rolling Stones. In 1995, the Microsoft Corporation paid them $2.5 million for the right to use their song, "Start Me Up," for the launch of Windows 95.

Employment Outlook

Most songwriters are unable to support themselves from their songwriting alone, and must hold other part-time or full-time jobs while writing songs in their spare time. The competition in this industry is extremely intense, and there are many more songwriters than paying projects. This situation is expected to continue into the next decade.

There are a few bright spots for songwriters. The recent rise of independent filmmaking has created more venues for songwriters to compose film scores. Cable television also provides more opportunities for song writing, both in the increase number of advertisements and in the growing trend for cable networks to develop their own original programs. Many computer games and software feature songs and music, and this area should grow rapidly in the next decade. Another potential boom area is the World Wide Web. As more and more companies, organizations, and individuals set up multimedia web sites, there may be an increased demand for songwriters to create songs and music for these sites. Songwriters with MIDI capability will be in the strongest position to benefit from the growth created by computer uses of music. In another field, legalized gambling has spread to many states in the country, a large number of resorts and theme parks have opened, and as these venues produce their own musical theater and shows, they will require more songwriters.

Success in songwriting is a combination of hard work, industry connections, and good luck. The number of hit songs is very small compared to the number of songwriters trying to write them.

Earnings

Songwriters' earnings vary widely, from next to nothing to many millions of dollars. A beginning songwriter may work for free, or for low pay, just to gain experience. A songwriter may sell a jingle to an advertising agency for $1,000 or may receive many thousands of dollars if their work is well known. Royalties from a song may reach $20,000 per year or more per song, and a successful songwriter may earn $100,000 or more per year from the royalties of several songs. A songwriter's earnings may come from a combination of royalties earned on songs and fees earned from commercial projects.

Those starting as assistants in music production companies or jingle houses may earn as little as $20,000 per year. Experienced songwriters at these companies may earn $50,000 per year or more.

Because most songwriters are freelance, they will have to provide their own health insurance, life insurance, and pension plans. They are usually paid per project, and therefore receive no overtime pay. When facing a deadline, they may have to work many more hours than eight hours a day or forty hours a week. Also, songwriters are generally responsible for recording their own demos, and must pay for recording studio time, studio musicians, and production expenses.

Conditions of Work

Songwriters generally possess a strong love for music, and regardless of the level of their success, usually find fulfillment in their careers because they are doing what they love to do. As freelancers, songwriters have control over how they spend their day. Often they work out of their own home or office. They will have their own instruments, and often their own recording equipment as well. They may also work in recording studios, where conditions can vary, from noisy and busy, to relaxed and quiet.

Writing music can be stressful. When facing a deadline, a songwriter may experience a great deal of pressure while trying to get their music just right and on time. At times, one's creativity seems to wane, and these periods can be extremely difficult to overcome. They may face a great deal of rejection before they find someone willing to publish or record their songs. Rejection remains a part of the songwriter's life, even after they become successful.

Many songwriters will work many years with limited or no success. On the other hand, songwriters experience the joys of creativity, which has its own rewards.

Sources of Additional Information

■ **American Guild of Authors and Composers**
40 West 57th Street
New York, NY 10019

■ **American Society of Composers, Authors, and Publishers (ASCAP)**
One Lincoln Plaza
New York, NY 10023
Tel: 212-621-6000

■ **Broadcast Music Inc. (BMI)**
320 West 57th Street
New York, NY 10019
Tel: 212-245-8986

For information on becoming a songwriter and becoming an association member, contact:

■ **Nashville Songwriters Association, International**
1025 16th Avenue South, Suite 200
Nashville, TN 37212
Tel: 615-256-3354

■ **National Academy of Songwriters**
6381 Hollywood Boulevard, Suite 780
Hollywood, CA 90028
Tel: 213-463-7178

■ **National Association of Composers USA**
Box 49652, Barrington Station
Los Angeles, CA 90049
Tel: 310-541-8213

■ **Songwriters and Lyricists Club**
PO Box 023304
Brooklyn, NY 11202-0066
Tel: 718-855-5057

■ **Songwriters Guild of America**
1500 Harbor Boulevard
Weehawken, NY 07087-6732
Tel: 212-686-6732

Stunt Performers

School Subjects
Physical education, Theater/dance

Personal Interests
Film and Television, Sports

Work Environment
Indoors and outdoors, Primarily multiple locations

Minimum Education Level
High school diploma

Salary Range
$25,000 to $75,000+

Certification or Licensing
None

Outlook
About as fast as the average

DOT
159

GOE
12.02.01

NOC
5135

Definition

Stunt performers, also called *stuntmen* and *stuntwomen,* are actors who perform dangerous scenes in motion pictures. They may fall off tall buildings, get knocked from horses and motorcycles, imitate fist fights, and drive in high-speed car chases. They must know how to set up "stunts" that are both safe to perform and believable to audiences. In these dangerous scenes, stunt performers are often asked to double, or take the place of, a star actor.

History

There have been stunt performers since the early years of motion pictures. Frank Hanaway, believed to be the first stunt performer, began his career in the 1903 film *The Great Train Robbery*. A former U.S. cavalryman, Hanaway had developed the skill of falling off a horse unharmed. Until the introduction of sound films in the 1920s, stunt performers were used mostly in slapstick comedy films, which relied on "sight-gags" to entertain the audience.

The first stuntwoman in motion pictures was Helen Gibson, who began her stunt career in the 1914 film series *The Hazards of Helen*. Chosen for the job because of her experience performing tricks on horseback, Gibson went from doubling for Helen Holmes, the star actress, to eventually playing the lead role herself. Among her stunts was jumping from a fast-moving motorcycle onto an adjacent moving locomotive.

Despite the success of Helen Gibson, most stunt performers were men. For dangerous scenes, actresses were usually doubled by a stuntman wearing a wig and the character's costume. Because films usually showed stunts at a distance, audiences could not tell the switch had been made.

Discrimination in the film industry also resulted in few minorities working as stunt performers. White men doubled for Native Americans, Asians, Latinos, and African-Americans by applying makeup or other material to their skin. This practice was called *painting down*.

As the motion picture industry grew, so did the importance of stunt performers. Because injury to a star actor could end a film project and incur a considerable financial loss for the studio, producers would allow only stunt performers to handle dangerous scenes. Even so, star actors would commonly brag that they had performed their own stunts. Only a few, such as Helen Gibson and Richard Talmadge, actually did.

Beginning in the 1950s a growth in the number of independent, or self-employed, producers brought new opportunities for stunt performers. In general, independent producers were not familiar with stunt work and came to rely on experienced stunt performers to set up stunt scenes and to find qualified individuals to perform them. Stunt performers who did this kind of organizational work came to be called stunt coordinators.

The Stuntmen's Association, the first professional organization in the field, was founded in 1960. Its goal was to share knowledge of stunt techniques and safety practices, to work out special problems concerning stunt performers, and to help producers find qualified stunt performers. Other organizations followed, including the International Stunt Association, the Stuntwomen's Association, the United Stuntwomen's Association, Stunts Unlimited, and Drivers Inc.

Because of these organizations, stunt performers are now better educated and trained in stunt techniques.

An increasing number of women and minorities have become stunt performers since the 1970s. The Screen Actors Guild (SAG), the union that represents stunt performers, has been at the vanguard of this change. In the 1970s SAG banned the practice of painting down, thus forcing producers to find, for example, an African-American stuntman to double for an African-American actor. SAG also began to require that producers make an effort to find female stunt performers to double for actresses. Only after showing that a number of qualified stuntwomen have declined the role can a producer hire a stuntman to do the job.

Over the years, new technology has changed the field of stunt work. Air bags, for example, make stunts safer, and faster cars and better brakes have given stunt performers more control. Stunt performers, however, still rely on their athletic ability and sense of timing when doing a dangerous stunt.

Nature of the Work

Stunt performers work on a wide variety of scenes which have the potential for causing serious injury, including car crashes and chases; fist and sword fights; falls from cars, motorcycles, horses, and buildings; airplane and helicopter stunts; rides through river rapids; and confrontations with animals, such as in a buffalo stampede. Although they are hired as actors, they rarely perform a speaking role. Some stunt performers specialize in one type of stunt.

There are two general types of stunt roles: double and nondescript. The first requires a stunt performer to double—or, to take the place of—a star actor in a dangerous scene. As a double, the stunt performer must portray the character in the same way as the star actor. A nondescript role does not involve replacing another person and is usually an incidental character in a dangerous scene. An example of a nondescript role is a driver in a freeway chase scene.

The idea for a stunt usually begins with the screenwriter. Stunts can make a movie not only exciting but also profitable. Action films, in fact, make up the majority of box-office hits. The stunts, however, must make sense within the context of the film's story.

Once the stunts are written into the script, it is the job of the director to decide how they will appear on the screen. Directors, especially of large, action-filled movies, often seek the help of a stunt coordinator. *Stunt coordinators* are individuals who have years of experience performing or coordinating stunts and who know the stunt performer community well. A stunt coordinator can quickly determine if a stunt is feasible and, if so, what is the best and safest way to perform it. The stunt coordinator plans the stunt, oversees the setup and construction of special sets and materials, and either hires or recommends the most qualified stunt performer. Some stunt coordinators also take over the direction of action scenes. Because of this responsibility, many stunt coordinators are members not only of the Screen Actors Guild but also of the Directors Guild of America.

Although a stunt may last only a few seconds on film, preparations for the stunt can take several hours or even days. Stunt performers work with such departments as props, makeup, wardrobe, and set design. They also work closely with the special effects team to resolve technical problems and ensure safety. The director and the stunt performer must agree on a camera angle that will maximize the effect of the stunt. These preparations can save a considerable amount of production time and money. A carefully planned stunt can often be completed in just one take. More typically, the stunt person will have to perform the stunt several times until the director is satisfied with the performance.

Stunt performers do not have a death wish. They are dedicated professionals who take great precautions to ensure their safety. Air bags, body pads, or cables might be used in a stunt involving a fall or a crash. If a stunt performer must enter a burning building, special fireproof clothing is worn and protective cream is applied to the skin. Stunt performers commonly design and build their own protective equipment.

Stunt performers are not only actors but also athletes. Thus, they spend much of their time keeping their bodies in top physical shape and practicing their stunts.

Requirements

There is no minimum educational requirement for becoming a stunt performer. Most learn their skills by working for years under an experienced stunt performer. A number of stunt schools, however, do exist.

Among the skills that must be learned are specific stunt techniques, such as how to throw a punch; the design and building of safety equipment; and production techniques, such as camera angles and film editing. The more a stunt performer knows about all aspects of filmmaking, the better that person can design effective and safe stunts.

Stunt work requires excellent athletic ability. Many stunt performers were high school and college athletes, and some were Olympic or world champions. Qualities developed through sports such as self-discipline, coordination, common sense, and coolness under stress are essential to becoming a successful stunt performer. Many stunt performers are college graduates.

Like all actors, stunt performers must belong to the Screen Actors Guild. Stunt performers who direct action scenes may also be members of the Directors Guild of America.

Because much of the work involves being a stunt double for a star actor, it is helpful to have a common body type. Exceptionally tall or short people, for example, may have difficulty finding a role.

Opportunities for Experience & Exploration

There are few means of gaining experience as a stunt performer prior to actual employment. Involvement in high school or college athletics is helpful, as is acting experience in a school or local theater. Some public libraries carry books on stunt performers and techniques.

Methods of Entering

Most stunt performers enter the field by contacting stunt coordinators and asking for work. Coordinators and stunt associations can be located in trade publications. Those who attend a stunt school may develop important contacts in the field.

Advancement

New stunt performers generally start with simple roles, such as being one of 40 people in a brawl scene. With greater experience and training, stunt performers can get more complicated roles. Some stunt associations have facilities where stunt performers work out and practice their skills.

About five to ten years of experience are usually necessary to become a stunt coordinator. Some stunt coordinators eventually work as a director of action scenes.

Employment Outlook

In the early 1990s there are a fewer than a thousand working stunt performers in the United States. About three hundred to four hundred are employed in Hollywood. Even among this small number, some are unable to find full-time work. Other significant places for stunt performers include New York, Florida, Arizona, and Texas. About 20 percent of stunt performers are women. Competition for available positions is fierce.

Employment opportunities are expected to remain extremely competitive throughout the 1990s and into the twentieth century. The availability of positions is tied in part to the number of action films made each year. The more action films the film industry makes, the more jobs become open to stunt performers.

Earnings

The earnings of stunt performers vary considerably by their experience and the difficulty of the stunts they perform. In the early 1990s the minimum daily salary of any member of the Screen Actors Guild, including stunt performers, is $466.

The Screen Actors Guild sets minimum daily salaries based on the overall cost of the motion picture being filmed. For low-budget films, those which cost under $2 million, the minimum daily salary for a stunt person is $466 per day, or $1,738 per week. For regular-budget films, those which cost more than $2 million to produce, stunt persons earn a minimum of $522 per day, or $1,946 per week. These minimum salaries were put into effect to ensure that a new or inexperienced stunt person received a guaranteed wage. However, more experienced stunt persons often negotiate a higher salary for their services.

Stunt performers are among the top wage earners in the Screen Actors Guild. One of the highest fees for a stunt, $150,000, was reportedly given to a man who in 1979 jumped off Toronto's 1,170-foot CN Tower and waited until he was only about 300 feet off the ground before releasing his parachute. Six-figure fees and such dangerous stunts, however, are rare. Because there are so few available positions, many stunt performers do not make enough money to stay in the field.

Stunt performers usually negotiate their salaries with the stunt coordinator. In general, they are paid per stunt; if they have to repeat the stunt three times before the director likes the scene, the stunt performer gets paid three times. The more elaborate and dangerous the stunt, the more money the stunt performer receives. Stunt performers are also compensated for overtime and travel expenses. Stunt coordinators negotiate their salaries with the producer.

Conditions of Work

The working conditions of a stunt performer changes from project to project. It could be a studio set, a river, or an airplane thousands of feet above the ground. Like all actors, they are given their own dressing rooms.

Careers in stunt work tend to be short. The small number of jobs is one reason, as are age and injury. Even with the emphasis on safety, injuries commonly occur, often because of mechanical failure, problems with animals, or human error. The possibility of death is always present. Despite these drawbacks, a large number of people are attracted to the work because of the thrill, the competitive challenge, and the chance to work in motion pictures.

Sources of Additional Information

■ **Screen Actors Guild**
7065 Hollywood Boulevard
Hollywood, CA 90028
Tel: 213-851-4301

■ **Stuntmen's Association of Motion Pictures**
4810 Whitsett Avenue
North Hollywood, CA 91607

■ **Stunts Unlimited**
3518 Cahuenga Boulevard West
Los Angeles, CA 90068
Tel: 213-874-0050

■ **Stuntwoman's Association of Motion Pictures**
PO Box 1922
Burbank, CA 91507

Index